Introduction

No one can dispute that one of the leaders in traction and 'big' tractors of years gone by was County Commercial Cars Ltd, formed in 1929. The small manufacturing firm was set-up by two brothers, Ernest and Percy Tapp, who joined engineering talent with a business mind to form a striving company.

Concentrating its early work on vehicles for the transportation of goods and military vehicles, post-war development saw the company look towards agricultural machines such as tracked crawlers.

One of the first developments in this field was known as the County Full-Track – a lightweight machine based on the Fordson E27N Major. This lead to a new direction and the company turned its attentions to agricultural and industrial machines.

Crawler production made way for tractors such as the famous 'Super-4' models of the 1960s, based on the Fordson Super Major; drive to the front axle was taken by twin propeller shafts from the rear axle of which the company is now famously recognised for.

A six-cylinder 'Super-6' soon followed and County continued to update its range on Ford's latest skid units. Export demand increased dramatically as did horsepower requirements and the company expanded rapidly to employ 475 people and cover a 10-acre site by the late Seventies.

On a high, the company launched its biggest tractor yet, the flagship 1884 based on Ford's 188hp TW-30. Although the

Richard Mason's 1963 County Hi-Drive was originally exported to Mexico to work on a celery farm.

tractor created much interest, County began to struggle in the recession and found it couldn't compete in the competitive export markets and sales dropped by almost half.

With Ford's decision to launch four-wheel drive models and horrendous bank rates, it was the final nail in the coffin and the company went into receivership in early 1983.

All was not lost however and the company continued under the instruction of David Gittins, a County dealer in Shropshire and later as the Benson Group that built a number of tractors in the early 1990s but struggled to find suitable cabs to meet the UK legislations.

The last tractors included the famous 'Ford 40 Series' based machines for the Falklands in 1995 and sadly no further machines were built.

Today the marque has a considerable following as Ford and Ford conversions are still at an all-time high on the enthusiasts' scene.

The County name now remains in the hands of Mark Osborne of Romsey in Hampshire who still provides parts and service back-up for tractors under-going renovation and not forgetting the many machines still working in both the United Kingdom and the rest of the world. ∎

Howard Sherren

GREATEST TRACTORS - County: 4WD Pulling Power

Published by

KELSEY PUBLISHING GROUP

Printed in England, United Kingdom by William Gibbon of Willenhall, West Midlands
on behalf of
Kelsey Publishing Limited,
Cudham Tithe Barn,
Cudham, Kent TN16 3AG
Telephone: 01959 541444   Fax: 01959 541400
www.kelsey.co.uk

©2011
ISBN 978-1-907426-16-2

GW00566932

With thanks to:
Dave Beare, Norman Chapman, Martin Gardener, Stuart Gibbard, Mike Gormley, Andrew Hall, Roger Hamlin, Kim Jackson, Peter Love, Chris McCullough, Robb Morgan, Mark Osborne, Howard Sherren, Peter D Simpson, Peter Small, Peter Squires, Adrian Tavernor, Andrew Tavernor, Roger Thomas, Bob Weir and Steve Wright.
Also a big thank you to the owners of all these fine tractors featured.
Visit the County Register at: www.county-tractors.co.uk

Contents

The Full-Track's original, under-powered petrol engine was soon replaced by the Perkins P6 diesel. Photo: Peter Love.

An in-road to agriculture

After noting its work with commercial vehicles, the Ministry of Agriculture considered County to be the right company to build a British-made crawler.

It was in 1948 that County Tractors finally completed its first tracked tractor based on the new Fordson E27N Major, which originally saw its release back in 1945. The E27N was a bid to keep abreast of the advances in agricultural technology and to replace the aging model N.

The management at Fordson in Britain wanted a new tractor – one that would build on the reputation that the company already enjoyed with British farmers. Unfortunately this came at a time when economic conditions were difficult, to say the least, as World War 2 had come to an end and there simply wasn't the money to invest in a 'from-scratch' model at Dagenham.

The obvious solution, therefore, was to build the Ford-Ferguson – a truly modern agricultural machine that couldn't be further apart from the Fordson N. This, however,

was still deemed economically unviable and the only option was to upgrade the existing model. The original model N's petrol engine was retained – but upgraded to a high-compression format.

The fact still remained, however, that the petrol unit was inadequate and its higher compression meant that it had a limited service life. This was further exacerbated by the fact that it had no cylinder liners and needed to be re-bored when it was worn out.

The prototype County Full Track (CFT) first emerged in 1948 using the petrol/tvo engine and was trialled on farms throughout the year before of a batch of 50 was delivered to the Ministry of Agriculture. It wasn't until the beginning of the following year that the crawler went officially on sale.

The E27N's rear differential was replaced by a solid axle with the crown wheel driven by the tractor's gearbox. The County used internal, expanding brake shoes, enclosed in brake drums to form the steering

clutches. By pulling on each lever; drive was disconnected from the relevant track.

When it came available the CFT was priced at £765 and the company was producing around 10 a day. However users found the 29bhp petrol engine lacked power and problems arose from oil starvation. On steep gradients the gravity fed system was not up to the job. This was rectified by fitting Perkins P6 six-cylinder diesel engines in 1948 increasing power to 45bhp and the price to £1,090.

Cast, spoked front idlers followed later and in 1951 the Model B CFT had strengthened track frames for industrial use. The E27N skid was replaced by the E1A Major and was then known as the 'Z' crawler, revealed at 1951's Smithfield Show.

The CFT, however, was made up to 1955 just for export, however it was very similar to the the replacement machine apart from a new six-speed gearbox and diesel, petrol and TVO options. ∎

A 1949 Fordson Major County crawler.

County Commercial Cars

Dave Beare records the diamond anniversary of County's first tractor.

County Commercial Cars Ltd manufactured County tractors and crawlers for over 35 years at Fleet in Hampshire and was one of those extraordinary British company success stories, growing from humble beginnings in 1929 to an £18 million turnover by 1977.

Brothers Ernest and Percy Tapp wanted to find a way of increasing the payload on middle-weight lorries and came up with a conversion that involved fitting an additional rear axle. This had been done many times before, but Ernest and Percy's extra axle was driven. The original lorry axle was replaced by a new one with a second pinion and a flange driving a short shaft at the back, connected to the extra axle located behind.

The conversion proved very successful, allowing considerably higher payloads to be carried with the bonus of improved traction.

Small-scale production of six-wheel conversions to Ford trucks with two driven rear axles soon got under way, these early experiences paving the way for all later 4x4 developments.

By virtue of hard work, frugality, ingenuity and sheer engineering skill the family-run business created an extensive range of successful machines (of which tractors were only a part) for agricultural, industrial, mining, forestry and a thousand other uses.

County tractors proved to be particularly successful in the timber trade as they were tough, would go practically anywhere and were very stable. Potato growers also liked them for their very low ground pressure and superior traction when working in soft ground conditions.

To most of us, the archetypal County tractor is a big blue and white 4x4 Ford-based unit with same-size front and rear wheels - although County produced many

Massey Ferguson, International and Leyland-based models.

The origin of these familiar machines can be traced to County's first tractor, the 1948 County Full Track, a narrow-gauge (34in) crawler based on the Fordson E27N Major. Five were built to an order from a Cambridge company, Pest Control, for use in hop-fields.

Following the success of these, the Tapp brothers began production of a standard-gauge crawler in 1949 and were soon making ten a week.

Many, many different crawler versions followed and it was not long before a customer requested a wheeled tractor with similar abilities.

In particular the sugar-cane industries in Puerto Rico had very specific needs, they wanted the performance of a crawler but with the ability to deliver up to 60 tons of cane to a refinery on a trailer by road and at reasonable speed. ➡

A 1954 Fordson Major Four-Drive.

County Commercial Cars was only too happy to oblige and came up with what amounted to a Mk3 crawler with wheels instead of tracks, the front pair being chain-driven from sprockets on the rear axle. It was named the County Four-Drive and was skid-steered, just like a crawler.

Few were sold in the UK, however, and in an attempt to broaden the appeal of its wheeled tractor, County developed the Super-4 derivative which was the company's first 4WD tractor with conventional front-wheel steering.

A prototype was up and running in 1960 and, from the beginning, featured County's unique 4WD transmission via twin prop-shafts, one for each front wheel. Power was taken forward from the final-drive unit, which meant the differential lock worked on all four wheels, as did the brakes.

A Super-6 followed and demand meant that the company was hard-put to meet orders. By 1975 turnover had reached £13 million.

County Commercial Cars dominated the British 4WD tractor market at the time, but Ford (which supplied most of the skid units) knew that if County could do it, it could too – and with greater commercial success, stemming from its immeasurably greater resources and financial muscle.

Other major tractor manufacturers soon followed suit and their combined sales had a devastating impact on County Commercial Cars. The small family-run company went bust, the failure being due to an unforeseen and unfortunate combinations of events.

The Four-Drive was a simple pulling machine. The Fordson Major's three-point linkage was removed and a heavy-duty drawbar replaced the standard unit.

A CCC conversion of a Ford lorry chassis with two driven rear axles.

A detail showing the drive-shaft taking power from the back of the front axle to the new rear axle. The front axle is torque-tube located, rear axle likewise, with ball-articulation on the rear of the front axle.

The high value of the pound destroyed traditional export markets, particularly in the Caribbean, a world recession meant overall sales plummeted 40 per cent, high interest rates prevented affordable borrowing and the decision by Ford and other tractor manufacturers to develop their own ranges of 4WD tractors to compete with County finally pushed County Commercial Cars Ltd over the edge.

The company went into receivership 25 years ago. In February 1983 the receivers sold the liquidated company to David Gittins, a County dealer from Shropshire, who founded a new company, County Tractors Ltd, to continue the business.

The entire stock of spares, part-completed tractors and untouched Ford skid units was all kept at Fleet, so whatever could be built was finished off and sold.

Around 20 County tractors were completed from stock in this way, after which County Commercial Cars Ltd concentrated on sourcing and supplying spares for the many thousands of County tractors still used and appreciated all over the world.

This invaluable County tractor spares service is still in operation.

County Tractors Ltd was taken over by the Benson Group in 1987, which relocated the business from Fleet to Knighton in mid-Wales, largely because the factory site in Hampshire was now worth a fortune.

A few tractors were made at Knighton but by 1990 production petered out – a small export order for 10 machines was filled in 1995, using Ford 40 Series skid units, but that was the end.

The spares department, meanwhile, had been kept by David Gittins and was relocated to Ludlow, but he'd had enough of tractors and passed on the County spare parts stock to Adrian Tavernor, who had been involved with County tractors since 1977.

Adrian owned the County Commercial Cars and County Commercial Engineers limited company names and ran the spares operation until he passed the baton to Mark Osborne of Romsey, Hampshire. ■

Swimming Super-Fours

One County version achieved worldwide fame and yet only a handful were ever made. The County Sea Horse was an amphibious Super-4, brainchild of David Tapp who personally steered the first, registered 999 HOR, into the history books as the only tractor ever to be driven across the Channel.

On July 30, 1963, he crossed from Cap Gris Nez to Kingsdown (near Dover) in 7 hours, 50 minutes at a respectable average speed of 3.5 knots.

Over a decade later David Gittins devised his own version of the County Sea Horse, using a County 754 with doubled-up wheels and floatation tanks. It demonstrated its abilities at the Ludlow Water Carnival in July 1978 where, nicknamed the "Teme Monster", it entertained carnival-goers by 'breaking down' and having to be 'repaired' by a 'service crew' in a rowing boat!

Adrian and Andrew Tavernor have also built an aquatic County 654 Super-4 which rejoices in the name "The Floater"...

A County childhood

Driving County tractors is one of the more memorable recollections that Northern Ireland enthusiast John Crothers can remember from his childhood. In fact, he and his brother George both learned to drive on this once famous tractor marque, as Chris McCullough found out.

"My father Sam used to have a small contracting business clearing scrubland," says John. "Originally he used an International Drott track dozer and some Fordson Majors in the business, but he later invested in a County Super-4 rubber wheeled tractor."

It was on this particular tractor in the late 1960s that both John and his brother George learned to drive. "This was the tractor that sparked my interest in County and Fordson tractors, an interest which has developed into quite an extensive County wheeled tractor and crawler collection."

After some time Sam Crothers founded a business in tipper truck haulage operating Leyland and Foden vehicles, followed later

by Volvo and Scania. Both sons took great interest in the trucks and learned to maintain and repair them but always maintained a strong interest in the County tractors. John later progressed to a job as a diesel mechanic with Ready Mix Concrete where he served his apprenticeship before switching to a career in motorsport preparation, a particular career move which spanned 20 years. With his immense interest in engines

Left: John Crothers on his 1961 County Clydesdale which bears serial number 1. This is one of only three known examples in existence and was purchased from a dealer in Scotland.

Below: An impressive sight. County launched the 1884 to the public at the 1980 Smithfield Show. This particular County 1884 is believed to have been the first to enter Northern Ireland.

This certainly made John's day as he was now the proud owner of a 1984 County 1884, serial number 49155, which complemented his collection nicely. "I was very happy to get my hands on the 1884 as this is the model every County collector dreams about," says John. "I carried out quite a bit of work on her including overhauling the front axle, a complete engine overhaul and fitting a new clutch. As I understand it, this County 1884 was the first one ever to enter Northern Ireland," he adds.

Object of attention
John's County 1884 rarely comes out of the shed, but when it does the attention it attracts is quite something. Usually destined for County working day demonstrations or the occasional ploughing exhibition when the 1884 is coupled up to a seven-furrow plough and is always the star of the show.

Also featured in John's rubber wheeled County collection is his favourite, a 1982 County 1474 TW based on the once-popular TW-20 tractor. Fitted with the County unique four-wheel drive system and 147hp engine this tractor is also "a very desirable model," according to John.

This particular example, bearing registration RIJ 5199, was bought new into Northern Ireland by a County Down cereal grower and is thought to be the only large County tractor purchased new in the country. This was another machine John pursued for a long time before being able to make the purchase. Also complementing John's portfolio is a 1960 County Super-4 with a Howard reduction gearbox, a very early example indeed from the Super-4 range. ➡

and mechanics the opportunity later arose for John to become involved with working on marine engines, an area where he spends most of his time currently.

Always on his mind!
Although tractor restorations and motorsport still form part of John's workload, County tractors were and are most certainly always at the forefront of his mind. Fuelled by his early interest in County tractors he decided in 1994 to start his own personal collection of rare County models, building up quite a range over the past 15 years.

A man on a mission, John always wanted to own the biggest County tractor ever built, the 1884 model, and pursued his dream until it became a reality. "I had heard of an 1884 working on a large vegetable farm in County Cork," he explains. "I began to monitor this particular County 1884 until finally one day I asked the owner if he would sell it, to which the response was 'yes.'"

This yellow 1962 County P55 Ploughman, powered by a four-cylinder 64hp engine is based on a Fordson Super Major and is a nice genuine example.

The latest addition to his collection is a 1964 County Super-4 tractor with blade attached which has been modified for use in the forestry industry. "I think this one was sold to the Netherlands when new and then moved on to Scandinavia before ending up in Scotland, where I bought her. I bought this tractor with the firm intention of restoring it, but if someone comes along before I get the chance, then it will be sold."

Major surgery!
Turning the attention to John's County Full Track collection, this is currently made up of six machines in the main collection with a few others in need of major surgery.

As well as a particularly rare extended Swamp crawler tractor, John has a 1959 Mark IV County crawler, based on a Power Major and fitted with a Bray angle dozer. "This one I bought in Wiltshire," he tells me. "It has actually been used to carry out a lot of work around the farm and I get a lot of pleasure driving it."

All John's crawlers are in true original condition, none more so than a very early 1952 County crawler Mk I fitted with 16 inch tracks purchased by John from Cambridgeshire.

This tractor was based on the Diesel Major and bears serial number 137. A nice 1959 County Ploughman P50 based on a Power Major adds a touch of class to the collection as well. "These were only built during a one year period. I bought this one in Cambridgeshire in as close to original condition as I have seen."

Next along the line-up was a yellow County Ploughman P55 based on a Super Major and built in 1962. "Powering up this crawler is a four-cylinder 64hp engine," he says. "This one is in nice original condition and came with a deluxe seat as standard."

The only other yellow crawler in the collection is a six-cylinder County CD50 thought to be only one of five in existence.

"It's really the equivalent specification to a County Super-6 rubber wheeled tractor," John explains. "It has a County fibreglass bonnet and an aluminium sump. Apparently it lay in an old lorry scrap yard for around 20 years before being resurrected by a collector. After replacing the battery she fired up first time."

A rare County CD50 six-cylinder crawler rated at 93hp is also part of John's collection. Apparently this one lay in a commercial vehicle breaker's yard for over 20 years before being rescued.

A favourite crawler

However, John's favourite crawler has to be his 1961 County Clydesdale which, according to the early serial number, would seem to be the first one ever built. "It is one of only two thought to be in existence today and is certainly my favourite," says John with a smile. "These were originally built as a cheap alternative for farmers and came with a front weight with 'County' inscribed on it. Amongst other things, it lacks a rev counter, hydraulics and a deluxe seat. I bought this one from a Scottish owner and it has pride of place in my collection as far as tracked models go," he adds.

John may have quite an extensive County collection but there still remain a few models he would like to make it complete, one of which is a yellow County CD50 crawler with blade, the other a County P6 crawler based on the Fordson Major E27N diesel. "I'd be interested in hearing from anyone who knows of one in good original condition," he says.

Just recently John has also invested in several Ebro tractors which are Spanish built based on the Fordson Major, and yes, some bearing County costumes. His huge interest in everything County has also rubbed off on

John's early County full track crawler, serial number 37, is based on a 1951 Diesel Fordson Major. This is the Mk I County version fitted with 16 inch tracks.

his son Elliott, who he says will inherit most of the collection one day. In the meantime John, who has undertaken quite a few County restoration projects for customers, will continue with his passion in everything County! ■

This 1982 County 1474 TW is what John describes as a "very desirable County tractor." This is the only large County tractor sold new into Northern Ireland. It spent its early days on a County Down arable farm and is John's favourite wheeled tractor in his collection.

Forestry Super Dexta

Martin Gardener tells us how he came to know a 1964 Super Dexta 4x4.

Nearly 20 years ago, on a family visit to Parkanaur Forest Park; near Dungannon, Northern Ireland I spotted a display of forestry equipment. These were mostly hand tools, various types of tree planting spades and early chainsaws, together with a photographic display.

However what really caught my eye was the tractor sitting outside. It was clearly based on a Fordson Super Dexta with a commissioning plaque confirming it was made by County. It was parked next to with another forestry tractor and plough, so I took a photo which ended up being tucked away in an album.

Ten years ago I saw an advertisement placed in *Tractor & Machinery* from Nick Gilbert of Devon requesting photographs of Ford four-wheel drive conversions, so I sent him a copy of the Super Dexta. I remember thinking at the time the tractor would make an interesting subject for an article. However after a few phone calls I found out that because of vandalism it had been removed to the Forestry Service main workshop at Hillsborough, near Belfast, so the idea got put on hold.

I subsequently received a phone call from Stuart Gibbard who had received a copy of my photograph from Nick Gilbert and wanted my permission to reproduce it for use in a forthcoming book. I was pleased to agree to this and we enjoyed a pleasant conversation in which I promised to take some more pictures of the County.

Several telephone calls later put me in touch with Blain Harrison, the area engineer at the Hillsborough workshop. I made arrangements to meet with him and view the tractor which was stored outside and a non-runner.

A day was taken off work in early August for the 70 mile trip. I arrived at the workshop and was met by Blain who although clearly a very busy but he graciously made the time to see me and moved a digger and a minibus that were boxing in the County so that I could inspect the tractor and take photographs. He then allowed me to have a good look around this fascinating place.

Since I had last seen it the County had deteriorated but was still a very interesting prospect. The engine and gearbox are standard Super Dexta with a transfer box fitted to the back of the gearbox. This

provided drive to the two axles and, by chain, to the twin-drum Ingland 2000 winch located to the rear of the roll over protection structure. The front half of the tractor, has articulated steering, the rear half consists of only the rear axle and two sets of rope fairleads mounted on top of a very hefty rear protection plate to prevent damage from timbers as they were towed across the site.

Both axles are fitted with 16.9x28 tyres. Although neither of the axles are Dexta items, I couldn't see any identifying plates on them, or in fact anywhere else on the tractor, except for the old type Northern Ireland registration number 7162 PZ, 1473215 and its Forestry Service number FD 0921.

The rear axle is fitted with drum brakes, which Blain later told me was the County's only real downfall as they filled with mud and left the brakes useless. This in turn led to overuse of the small transmission handbrake, which broke a similar problem that affected

the Mercedes-Benz Unimogs that were used at a later date.

Unlike most articulated-steer vehicles which have a centre pinion allowing the two halves to swivel on uneven ground, the County has a completely rigid frame and only the front axle swivels. This axle is mounted at the back of a substantial A-frame; and is fitted with the pinion pointing steeply upwards and not directly at the transfer box.

The front universal joint therefore runs at a very sharp angle, causing speed variations of the pinion. I don't understand the reasoning for mounting the axle in this manner but it does not seem to have affected the reliability and was trouble free in service.

The steering is of simple design, the left-hand drop arm is disused but the right-hand arm has a rod running back to a spool valve mounted on the back half of the machine and a double acting ram on the right side of the frame.

The advantage of this system is when the steering wheel is turned just a little the ram starts to operate and the distance between the two frame halves on the right-hand side either increases or decreases. In the process it automatically closes the spool valve so the steering doesn't continue on to full lock. I tried the steering to see if it was very light, but it appeared to be well weighted.

A small crankshaft driven pump activates the steering and hydraulic blade fitted to the front. Once again the small prop-shaft driving the pump is also inclined in a down ward direction at a very steep angle.

After taking my photographs I took up Blains offer to take a look at some of the other interesting items around the yard. Another County, a crawler based on the Super Major with a Winsam cab was located behind the Dexta. This looked to be in quite good condition and was fitted with 30inch wide swamp tracks. In order to extend the track length which assists in reducing ground pressure and stability, a spacer has been fitted between the gearbox and the back section of the transmission.

The other tractor in the yard had actually been in the background of my original photo and is a Garrett, but not from the famous company in Leiston, Suffolk. Blain told me it was built in Canada and was in use around the same time as the other County. It is in many ways alike in concept, but simpler.

The Garrett is powered by a Fordson Diesel Major engine which would have produced a little more power than the County, but apparently its single-drum winch was a drawback for forestry work. The steering on this tractor is really simple and conducted with a large lever located between the legs connected to a spool valve. This is pushed to the left or right in accordance with the direction of travel.

At the end of my visit I just had time to ask Blain a few last questions and thank him for his co-operation. He told me he believes that there were six of the County Dexta's built to this design and the Northern Ireland Forestry Service had two of them, but he ➡

The County Super Dexta was sold at the Cheffins vintage sale in April 2010.

didn't recall the fate of the second one. The one I looked at had previously been restored by Lisburn College many years ago but sadly lying outside had taken its toll. Hopefully somebody will soon return it to its original condition again.

I had a further conversation with Stuart Gibbard, who told me it is believed that in fact there were only three tractors of this type built. The first, a prototype, is thought to be in Scandinavia, while the two production models were supplied to the Northern Ireland Forestry Service.

The story has continued since then with the tractor being sold in April 2010 in non-running condition at a Cambridgeshire auction. Had the tractor been stored undercover it may have been in better condition but even so it created a good amount of interest.

One bidder, Alan Kelly, was stuck in New Zealand owing to the Icelandic volcanic ash cloud. He had got as far as Singapore when the County Super Dexta came under the hammer, but fortunately his bid was successful and he became its proud new owner.

Despite its current state, he is making every effort to get it running in time for future shows. ∎

Despite its age and the nature of work it undertook, the Super Dexta-based County has stood the test of time well.

Valentine's Day splash

Taking time off from any romantic commitments, our correspondent travelled to Gloucestershire to see Martin Fernihough drive his tractor in a lake, in aid of charity.

Martin Fernihough is a unique kind of guy; he has a 'British Bulldog' attitude to life. This is something that is gradually being droned out of most of us, with more rules and regulations coming daily from Europe and other places. He likes to live life to the full and make the most of whatever is going on.

Born the youngest in a farming line, life was all about competing against his elder brothers and eventually he went on to be a success at Auto Grass and Stock Car racing. But mechanical skill is what Martin is all about, and from a pig farmer's assistant he started in agricultural repairs on Fordson Majors and the like. As time went on he went contracting, grubbing out woods and doing drainage work using a Bristol Europa and Taurus MK1 and Mk2.

Martin then went into the skip business with a Bedford KM, which he developed with a demountable cable/hydraulic lift system, which he has become famous for. People liked what they saw so Martin sold them what they wanted.

He went on to create the next example with a Ford D1000 chassis, and a turbocharger fitted to the Ford six-cylinder engine, featuring the multi-lift system body.

Martin has become famous for his company, BaS LIFT, and his daughter Gemma is his successful business manager. They build the system onto a range of reconditioned chassis' making it very cost effective along the way, particularly for smaller-sized operations.

The company exports the system all over the world, either as flat beds, or as a skip system. ➡

Moving down to the water the Sea Horse passes the large assembled crowd.

Martin fires up 'Gizmo' and we are off to the lakes for the afternoon bonanza.

They had been loaded flat on the ground, before being strapped down to the flat bed and then lifted on to the back of the truck. Certainly a most satisfactory system to use and safer than driving up a steep ramp, that's for sure.

Martin's latest project has turned out to be as a publican at his local, the Wheelbarrow and Castle. The licence to this hostelry was last held by his family in 1910 and he wasn't going to see the place die, so he took it on. Although the Wheelbarrow and Castle Public House does do good food, Martin says it's the beer that counts, and he is developing this side of things with real ales and such like.

"There is nowhere to go these days for a good old drink", he says, "so this is the place to go in the area and we are working to build this side of the business up".

Gizmo the 38 tonner

Martin is a well known Fordson tractor owner with his Doe Triple-D New Performance Major. However Martin and his team created the ultimate in towing tractors with 'Gizmo' that's based on an ERF E10 with 14 litre Cummins power.

Martin named it after something out of the famous 'Mad Max' films, with its Eaton gearbox and Rockwell axles the 38 tonner is something very special. It has changed colour a few times and now is in a mid blue livery. It's a superb piece of engineering and makes the ultimate pulling tug as was seen at the 'Valentine's Day Splash'.

County Sea Horse

With his interest in 'oddities' and engineering challenges, Martin showed a close interest in the County Sea Horse that was offered for sale by Cheffins in November 2007 (Malcolm Beaton 4x4 tractor sale in Somerset).

This was a former Wilson of Castle Douglas, Scotland 1963 County Sea Horse Super-4 that had been sold to Malcolm at the 2006 Cheffins spring collective for just over £6,000.

Martin successfully bid for the tractor at the sale, and then carried out a complete rebuild in his famous workshop.

The tractor made its debut on the last day of February 2009 at the Tractor World Show, Malvern, to critical acclaim – with its new floatation tanks, totally rebuilt back end, panel work overhaul, fresh yellow paint and sign writing.

The Sea Horse is unloaded down by the lake, which all went well.

But will it float?

However it had not been tested in the water and this was conveyed to Martin by his good friend Phil Collins of contracting combine fame while having a pint or two in the Wheelbarrow and Castle. Martin said "if you find me a big enough lake the Sea Horse will be ready."

Phil came back to him, much to Martin's surprise, and said that Bishampton fishing lakes at the Vale golf course were up for it, especially if it was for charity. When Martin's wife Marilyn heard all about this, she had to remind her husband of many years that he does not swim. Naturally plenty of buoyancy gear was purchased for Martin to wear, just in case the Sea Horse decided to sink.

It was decided that Sunday 14 February, Valentine's Day, would be the big day to test out the tractor. They had heard all about what County sales supremo David Tapp achieved on 30 July 1963, when he travelled from France to St Margret's Bay on the east Kent coast in 7 hours 50 minutes.

He then went on to plough a field not far from Deal, Kent. But how would Martin's outfit get on? Particularly considering the fact that the tractor had been rebuilt and not tested in water. Before the fateful day however, Martin had tested the tanks and made sure that everything was waterproof.

It was decided to mark the occasion by a tractor road run starting from the Wheelbarrow & Castle Public Inn to the fishing lakes at Bishampton. A staggering 48

Martin gets all hitched up with his heavy-duty buoyancy life jacket.

tractors paid £10 each to take part and, with further donations, just over £900 was raised for the local air ambulance. A wonderful achievement!

At 2pm 'Gizmo' led the party to the water's edge where the star of the day, the County Sea Horse Super-4, was unloaded from Martin's Ultimover 10 trailer. As ➡

Still in contact with solid ground, but not for long...

Left: We are away! The propeller and reversed tyres working in unison to move the County through the water. Martin appears to be in his element and in full control.

Gemma Fernihough describes it, the scene resembled one from the Pied Piper but instead of a magic flute it was a fog horn making all the noise! Had they come to see a man 'doggy' paddle back to the shore with 'egg all over his face' or a Sea Horse floating serenely across the water? It would all be sorted out in a short space of time all in front of some 200 people who had come to witness it first hand.

The unloading went well and the County was running fine as it came off the trailer. Martin was all geared up and after some adjustments was to hit the calm lake, rather different to what David Tapp encountered on 30 July, but similar to when they started the Sea Horse trials.

To rapturous applause the 55hp tractor went down into the water, which got deeper and deeper, and at the same time Martin was going lower and lower and things were getting rather worrying for him. He was thinking that in those pictures 47 years ago David was not as low as this in the water, and he could swim!

Martin wanted to change into a lower gear but was not sure what the outcome would be, so left it where it was. However he feels sure that if the wheels had not been turning quite so fast, better traction would have been achieved and therefore a higher buoyancy level all-round. More experiments are to be tried in the future!

Having completed the task, the Sea Horse did a powerful victory lap causing the ripples of the waves to climb high around the bank side. It then rose serenely out of the water and back onto dry land to a roar and raptuous applause from the excited and dedicated crowd. They had witnessed a wonderful sight and something that will be long remembered. Again it showed that true 'British Bulldog' sprit that Martin Fernihough possesses.

A Channel crossing?
Following the success of this event, it has got Martin thinking about a full re-enactment of the 28-mile English Channel crossing. Now the person he wants to pilot the tractor is none other than Lieutenant Commander Michael Fernihough, his brother, who these days resides in the West Country... by the sea!

This is a wonderful idea for the 50th anniversary, but for now congratulations to everyone involved. It was a wonderful, never to be forgotten, day.

We thank Bill Cowley and the Fernihough family for their help in the preparation of this article. ■

Martin is seen on his victory lap of the lakes and is heading for the shore.

The unique County Four-Drive. Photo: Peter Love.

Four-Drive revolution

Equal wheeled four-wheel drive tractors had not been taken seriously until the chain-driven County Four-Drive came along in 1954.

Marshall of Gainsborough successfully developed its Fowler VF crawler into the Field-Marshall Series 3 tractor and County was keen to do the same with its CFT E27N crawler.

The introduction of the Fordson E1A, however, saw the CFT E27N evolve into the model Z – a very successful machine that was used as the basis for the Four-Drive.

This new type of tractor utilised a chain and sprocket drive from the rear to front drive hubs, lubricated in an oil bath housing. This, as time went on, tended to leak and when abused the chain jumped off the sprocket causing grief and for all concerned. The time it consumed the fitter taking the oil

bath cover off, sorting the Reynolds chains out and putting it all back and refilling the oil was a struggle to keep up with at times. In other words the drive mechanism did need more development, but that was to come later in the 60's with the Super-4 and Super-6.

Getting back to the pioneering Four-Drive, it didn't have a differential and relied on the steering clutches and brakes to manoeuvre it as such, which again caused pressure on the 'flimsy' drive system.

Not many were sold on the home market as this example was, remembering it carries the rare to find three-point linkage and is part of the fabulous Richard Mason collection in East Anglia. The original County objective was to build a good

pulling tractor for the sugar cane industry, particularly in South America, West Indies, Queensland, Australia and South Africa, which were for so many years an excellent market for County.

In 1958 the Four-Drive was improved, as was the P50 Ploughman crawler with multi-plate clutches, and was sold mainly to the plant and machinery market. A number of this model have survived with the angle dozer blade, which was offered as a separate model until 1962 and supplied mostly in plant yellow.

It's a very desirable model which a number of collectors are always looking for, and attracts great interest at any show or working event today. It was certainly a revolutionary machine for its time. ∎

A magnificent restoration and a source of pride for its owner Richard Mason and the man who did the work, John Crothers (pictured).

Saving Grace

Chris McCullough discovers an amazing, and historic, Super-4 restoration.

An eventful and colourful life involving demonstration trips to Germany and The Netherlands, and a long service in the agricultural and forestry industries eventually took their toll on this County Super-4 tractor – so much so that it was almost deemed beyond repair.

However, this tractor secretly held a unique history that was to be its saving grace when current owner Richard Mason from Lincolnshire purchased it in the Shropshire area.

It carries serial number 11483 which, according to the County records, makes it the second Super-4 built on a Fordson Super Major tractor. The records show this one has a build date of October 17, 1961, and that it

enjoyed quite a colourful history moving from UK to Germany to The Netherlands and then eventually back to Bennetts of Baldock, a then-Ford dealership in England.

The foreign trips are thought to coincide with demonstration trips to Europe but it was a long and dedicated service to the agricultural and forestry industries that wore out the County Super-4 to near-scrap condition. ➡

The Fordson Super Major-based Super-4 prior to restoration.

County and Ford collector Richard Mason was so inspired by the tractor's history and the fact that it was the second County Super-4 built on a Super Major, that he decided to completely restore it, preserving not only the tractor but its historic relevance as well.

Richard had several conversations with County enthusiast and restorer John Crothers from Glenwherry, just outside Ballymena in Northern Ireland. Following viewings of some of John's previous restorations Richard decided it was he who should carry out this vital work.

John himself also has quite a County collection and was delighted but he is not only a tractor enthusiast but also a marine engineer and had to fit in the County restoration around his work on the ferries.

The brief given to him when he started the work in 2007 was that the tractor had to be restored to original condition, without compromise.

John said: "This County was worthy of a proper restoration with all original parts. It received a total nut-and-bolt restoration commencing with a total stripdown and complete overhaul of the engine, which was refitted with all new engine components and ancillary parts.

"The front axle system was next on the restoration schedule and also received a total overhaul. Drive shafts and drive take-offs on these Countys are always problematic, needing special attention to leave them right.

"The original shafts themselves were worn beyond use and no replacements could be found so we had to completely remanufacture new ones from detailed engineering drawings at a considerable cost."

This tractor was most probably a prototype model initiated before full production began. John noted during the restoration that quite a few components

All that glitters isn't necessarily gold; it can be blue!

were different to those of the later production model which ran through until 1964-1965.

With most of the mechanical restoration work completed John then assembled most of the main chassis, engine and hydraulics together as a unit sitting on axle stands.

"A test programme was then carried out over a period of three days running the tractor at various speeds in all gears to test that the engine, transmission and hydraulic systems were completely tight and free from oil leaks.

"With this test completed and any adjustments made, some components were removed again. All parts were then sand-blasted, painted and rebuilt again. By doing it this way I can ensure all parts receive individual attention and are blast-cleaned right back to base metal, primed, undercoated and gloss finished. Special grit is used in my own sand-blasting equipment to ensure the correct finish for painting. I

A final run in Northern Ireland before the County heads for England.

prefer to do all my own sand-blasting in order to prevent damage to components by outside sand-blasting companies," said John.

With all the parts painted and assembled John's attention turned to the electrics where he fitted all-new lights and rewired the entire system. New instruments and County badges were also fitted to the near-completed project.

"Most of the new parts including the mudguards, nosecone lights and grilles came from my own store of original parts that I have built up over the years," added John. "The fact that this tractor has such a colourful and important history warranted a complete and original restoration using as many new, original parts as required.

"Some of the parts took considerable time either to restore or remanufacture. For example, the badges take a long time to restore back to original condition. The entire emphasis on this restoration from the very

beginning was attention to detail without compromise.

"Although the restoration began some three years ago, it was around February 2010 that Richard decided he wanted to host his own private display of his collection. A big push was necessary to complete the project in time for his show," said John.

Indeed, the County Super-4 restoration was only completed the day before the show and was loaded on to a lorry which caught the last ferry out of Belfast that night. The County arrived home to its owner on the afternoon prior to the evening event.

Richard expressed his pleasure in viewing the tractor for the first time in three years. He said: "It looks absolutely marvellous indeed."

This latest addition to his collection received full praise from all those who attended his private show. His newly-restored County Super-4 fits in well with the rest of his superb collection and was a fitting tribute to the Super Major's 50th anniversary. ■

New instruments were part of the restoration.

Chunky tyres and wheel weights all-round give the Super-4 tremendous traction.

Country's top County?

George Crothers owns what is probably the best County in Northern Ireland, writes Chris McCullough.

aving a brother with a keen interest in County tractors has rubbed off on George Crothers from Kilwaughter in County Antrim, who is now the proud owner of a very original Super-4 model.

George's brother John has quite a collection of County tractors and crawlers, but both men agree the 64hp Super-4 is something special.

Still in completely original condition this particular County model was first purchased not far from its current home, as George explained.

"Its first owners were Clinty Quarries who are situated close to Ballymena, which isn't that far away from here. It was sold to the quarry by dealership Coulters of Belfast on February 24, 1964, and supplied to them by County tractors of Fleet in Hampshire."

This County Super-4 (serial number 13394) was sold with a Bomford dozer blade

The three-point linkage is aided by an assistor ram and above this rests the air tank for the brakes.

It was from one of these that George bought it in the early '90s in very original condition.

"Clinty Quarry is well known for its excellent attention to machinery. The company has a fully-equipped workshop up there where all machines are well looked after and serviced," said George.

"The County Super-4 today is in extremely good original condition, which is a fine testament to the mechanics at the quarry. It turns out my particular model is one of the last ever Super-4 models built as it has the blue and grey livery.

"Over the years of my ownership I have taken the blade off and put it into storage, fitted larger 14x30 wheels back on, and that's it."

George is workshop foreman for a local transport company and has a strong interest in trucks - so much so that he has his own vintage 1974 Atkinson tractor and trailer unit. But tractors still feature in his collection, which includes other County models and a Ploughmaster - and the County Super-4 is certainly his favourite.

"I take her out to some road runs and rallies and to every County tractor working day staged here in Northern Ireland but the highlight for me was taking her to the world record tractor gathering at Cooley," he said. ■

The business-end of the braking system.

attached to the front and was used for keeping the quarry tidy.

It also had another quite unusual feature - "This particular model was sold with 14x24 eight-ply Dunlop tyres but was later fitted with solid wheels to avoid punctures around the quarry.

"It also features a proper Ford-fitted vacuum braking system, which uses air vacuum instead of air pressure to operate the brakes – a system not too commonly found today.

"This tractor spent many years working around the quarry before being sold on to a construction company in Ballymena and then appeared at a couple of tractor dealerships over a period of time."

The Super-4's Goodyear tyres definitely add to the tractor's imposing stance.

The tyres were evenly worn, showing the fact that the steering was in reasonably good order.

A restoration project

Grahame Cluley, a trained engineer, first bought his County 754 in 2005 to use on the paddock. Perhaps it was inevitable that he would treat to a thorough restoration. We take a step-by-step look at the project.

Former Pedigree Pet Foods project engineer Grahame Cluley from Oakham, Rutland likes 'big things' he used a Fordson Dexta to mow the paddock where his wife Sally keeps her horses. However the tractor wasn't big enough for Grahame, neither did it have the power and engineering prowess that he was looking for.

He got chatting with friends from the Vale of Belvoir Club, and they suggested a classic Ford 4x4. At the same time, in the pages of *Tractor & Machinery*, an ex-Welsh forestry County 754 was spotted for sale.

So, in early 2005 a trip was made to see what turned out to be a 1970 'monster from the deep.' The engine chucked out a pint of oil from the exhaust while they were just looking at it.

A deal was done at a good price, knowing the engine was in need of major work. However, generally the tractor, based on the 5000 skid unit, was in reasonable order.

Another thing Grahame liked was the original 1970 Duncan cab.

Getting her working
It was in June 2005 when Grahame took the tractor to his workshop and stripped the engine out. A couple of companies were involved here and new liners, pistons, crank regrind, camshaft bearings, injectors and injector pump overhaul were all part of the process.

The job was completed by Marshall's, part of the Peck group of companies, who are steeped in New Holland history today.

With the tractor running a pick-up hitch was acquired to the original specification and it was time to use the 754 with a McConnell mower, working on the neighbouring farm. It turned out to be great fun and gave Grahame the chance to find out what else was wrong with the tractor.

The full works
Other things then got in the way including finishing off the house that he had built.

Being an engineer at heart, things started to niggle him about the tractor and he eventually decided he was going to rebuild it from head to toe.

Essentially the object was to have it back to what it was like when new and keeping it authentic as possible, with the right type of parts for the model and so on. The story of Grahame's restoration is told through excellent pictures taken all the way through the process. The photos were very useful for Grahame as they helped him know where things were to go. He says that a workshop manual is essential if you have never worked on one of these machines before.

Grahame hadn't, and if you don't know, it's useful to ask a County expert or two for the answer. They are around, and can be very helpful. Most of the parts for the restoration came from Mark Osborne in Hampshire, who has great knowledge on the subject.

The end result successfully debuted at the gloriously-hot Belvoir Castle Rally. It stood out from the crowd and was to take the Club's award at the show as well.

Now with the tank out the way one could start to access the wiring and fuel pipes that were to be renewed.

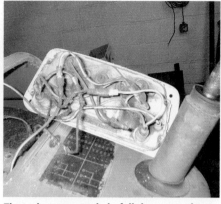

The tachometer needed a full clean up and sort out as did the wiring in this area.

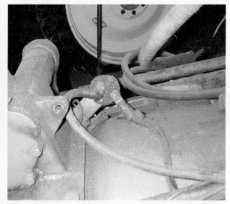

Cut off switch – One thing that was to be left off when it came to sorting the electrics out was the cut off switch as it was not needed this time.

It's amazing where the wires fitted through, as can be seen here, one has to get it right when the tractor is assembled again.

All jacked up on hard wood blocks safe to work on all aspects of the tractor with this near-side view.

A considerable amount of work on the axles and hubs was required, but it was a clean down job that was needed first to ascertain the full requirements to bring them up to specification.

With the cab removed for full restoration, having used the telehandler to lift it off, one can fully get down to the job in hand, particularly the front to rear drive-shaft universal joints.

With the prop-shaft removed, it was found that the end flange on the n/s differential drive flange was worn inside, creating the oil leak on the unit that you can see in the picture.

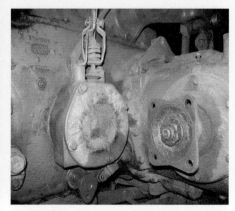

Looking from the other end with the prop-shaft removed we see that the transmission hand brake is burnt out by the missing paint from the end of cover, which has got very hot indeed.

Now right underneath the tractor we see the under beam front axle main pivot pin, which had 35mm of play in it and was going to need major work to get right.

Looking at the back end now we see the full linkage that came with the tractor, however it was very worn out in more ways than one and was going to take lots of parts and money. ➡

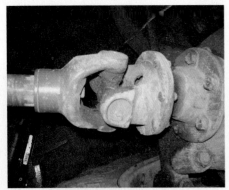

It's a hereditary problem, but all four-wheel drive tractors of the 50-80's suffer from universal joint failure and need to be regularly greased, the Hardy Spicer joints were to need the works.

Even to undo the nyloc nuts and bolts took lots of torque on the socket and ring spanner. Always fit new nyloc nuts and bolts when reassembling the joints and do retighten after a short road test.

Eventually it came undone to reveal the wear in the flange that had created the oil leak over time.

Undoing the companion flange, which was very tight on the splines, but with the use of the copper hammer came undone.

The companion flange was very worn and instead of metal spraying the surface and turning it back, the flange was turned down resleeved, pressed on with Loctite and was like new again.

Graham didn't have a press himself, so farmed the universal joint replacement job out. The joints were so tight that they had to be carefully burnt out on the yokes with oxygen and acetylene.

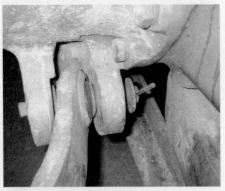

Back on the linkage the front pins and bushes were very worn and had to be replaced, but took some getting out to say the least. It is essential to keep original type parts at all times.

If you are not sure how the linkage goes then place it on the floor in the correct position and photograph as required. However the essence was it was well worn and needed the full works.

Lower link pin and original type tapered safety pin, which are hard to find these days and need to be in good condition to use again. They are not the same as the safety clip that is commonly used these days.

Now all pulled apart the brake shaft, disc and the oil seal, which was replaced as were the linings and generally overhauled.

This assembly had to all be replaced and you can see now why it didn't all work.

Ready to start the assembly with the spiral bevel gear to go in first.

Now all back together with the new oil seal and new paint on the transmission housing.

On goes the housing the build up begins again, with care not to damage things.

All the internal parts in place, except for the lifting arm, with copper slip in the relevant parts.

While Graham had the bonnet on the floor he pulled the paint off with paint stripper to reveal the lettering to finally confirm the tractor to be a County 754 model.

Back to the transmission with the top removed the hydraulic pump could be viewed.

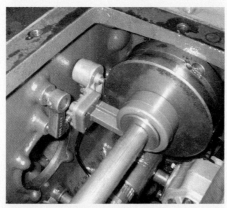

The pto engage and brake mechanism was to be a bit of a problem as it would not stop properly at all.

All in the air and ready to be fitted back with the return filter all in place.

It's all ready to fit back on the transmission main housing again.

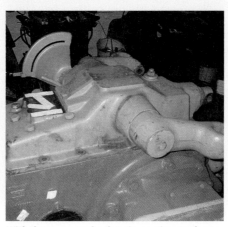

With the top cover back on it was time to clean and pull the paint off, then etch primer for a start.

It had to be all pulled apart as the pto brake would not stop on the rim properly, in fact the brake arm had to be straightened out to solve the problem, not curved around as one would have thought. ➡

All etch primered by brush along with the rest of the skid unit, while the panels were sprayed.

How about this then! Look at the shape of the track rod it should be straight and is of the earlier tube type construction. These were a problem, bent very easily and were replaced with a solid rod construction as in this case.

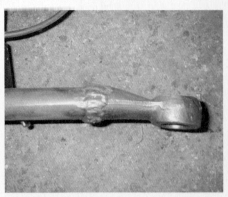

Actuating cylinder end - As can be seen the end of the actuating cylinder has been welded up. Graham rewelded the damaged area and dressed it up properly.

Track rod end – New gaiters went on the track rod ends that were in excellent condition, the original types are not available today, but it's hardly noticeable.

Front stub axle removal was not made easy because of the awkward shape and finding its centre of gravity.

On strip down of the stub axle the driving pinion pilot bearing was found to be damaged so was replaced.

Seals have to be soaked in the appropriate oil before installation. These are still made of leather!

The seals were pressed in place with a home-made wooden dolly turned on a lathe by a friend.

The stub axle is retained in place with three bolts plus the security of a tab washer.

Lowering the front axle frame underneath the tractor. This required jacks and blocks at three points to achieve the objective and not jam the front pivot between the side bars.

Axle front pivot cover removed. The face of this cover has thin plastic shims to adjust the float, it looks as though at one time this has been too tight with the amount of pick up on the faces.

Pivot showing the worn bush. The bronze bush which sits over the steel bush was nearly worn through. The loose ring is the sealer here that sits tight up against the pivot.

The pivot faces are very hard and were cleaned up as best as possible using a diamond stone which I would normally use for the TCT tips on router cutters!

Steering box had to be resealed due to a weep of oil at the base, which took some time to sort out.

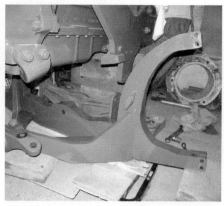

Steering axle frame was moved under the skid unit using a car creeper trolley. Both pivots are in place ready to bolt to the skid unit.

Steering axle jacked up into place showing the pivots for the stub axle.

Stub axle lifted into place, note the cloths everywhere so the finished paintwork was not damaged.

Completed and back in, and after a brush paint job it's ready to go working again.

Second time around in January 2010 the engine has the manifold and other sundry items removed for the major rebuild, but at least the engine is in excellent first class order.

With the engine run in and no problems having arisen it was all down to a good scrape and clean up, ready to be hand painted with Old 20 Parts paint, which Graham Cluley recommends.

A new lift pump was needed, making sure the cam on the Simms pump is in good order. The fuel pipes were also replaced and look very straight and neat, just as it should be.

It's always a good idea to have a drain bowl underneath the fuel filter on the engine for collection of the excess fuel. Always change the top ring on the filter housing, this is essential.

In respect to the power steering pump its again a good thing to clean it out and replace the 'O' ring every time you service the tractor as it will save any chance of future leaks.

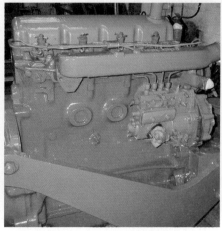

Now all painted up and ready to add all the components back on for the final rebuild. ➡

Always replace the oil, and the screw on oil filter ever year if you are just using the tractor for rallying. Do not skimp on low grade oils either. Treat your tractor well.

Many parts were painted and installed. Our efforts at spray painting resulted in solvent pop which we could not cure so matching 2-pack paint was sorted and the panels sprayed by Ben Craig.

New gaiters were fitted to the steering ram but the ram itself was in good condition. Gaiters were also fitted to the track rod ends although these were not original. However scouring the many auto shows and tractor events came up with a near match.

Whilst the skid unit was without the final body panels the cab frame had a trial fitting with new bushes and pins, again all the cloths in place to prevent scratching.

The pedals were in a bad state as the treads were worn through and the linkage to lock the pedals was ineffective. I don't know how this linkage was derived or how it was supposed to work, I decided to go back to the original Ford design.

First I made a former with a series of holes in the same pitch as the original holes.

A piece of sheet steel was clamped to the former with small holes the same pitch as the original.

Each hole was then heated to red heat and using a large centre punch was hit to form the tread. The amount of hitting required and the size of the small hole was tested beforehand.

When all the eight holes were formed the small bend in the tread was formed and the steel cut to size to fit the pedal. The brakes were prepared and painted and fitted.

The drive shafts with new universal joints, bushes and oil seals were refitted. It's important that the splined shaft and the housing are aligned together with the marks on the shaft and housing plus the universal joints also aligned together as well.

With the pedals and shaft now fitted the footplates can be put in place.

The tractor was changed back from an alternator to a dynamo to provide the proof meter drive.

Wheels and tyres

Two of the rims had Bettinson lugs welded to them which had at some time in the past been used to attach dual wheels to them. A total of 10 lugs were removed without damaging the rim. The use of dual wheels had caused another problem which revealed itself when the rim was shot blasted, cracks around the circumference of the rim in the vicinity of the lugs. The rims and centres were refurbished by Ben Craig to a point where the final coat of paint was required. At this point the tyre was fitted and the tyre masked on both sides, getting the tape between the tyre and the rim is the secret to a good job.

Mudguards

The mudguards were modified from the original design so that the water running down the inside did not all drain onto the footplate. This was a common cause of rotting the mudguards and a collection point for general debris as well.

Duncan cab

At this point the tractor was ready for the cab to be fitted. When it was purchased it had a ¼in thick steel plate fully welded onto the frame as a roof structure. It took two days with a grinder and great care to remove the plate without damage to the cab frame.

The doors were stripped of the glass and plastic windows. Here the catches were removed before the door was straightened using both brute force and delicate tweaks. The door was fully stripped of paint, filled, primed and set aside.

The front window of the tractor was plastic and so scratched it was difficult to see objects on the other side, probably OK in the forest but not good on the roads. A window was eventually found at Robert Wraight's near Ashford, Kent. A slightly-damaged, but repairable, fibreglass roof was also acquired from the same place.

The side sliding windows were absolutely solid with the aluminium anodising bubbled through.

The refurbishment of the cab came about 2½ years after the original start. The frame was prepared for painting with the filling of all the holes, dents and scrapes and the holes drilled for the wiring.

The cab was now stripped of all its accessories and painted with 2-pack paint.

Summary

Since the major work on the tractor, it has done over 200 miles of road work either towing the threshing drum, attending rallies or just enjoying a day out with it.

Grahame has since had a cab step added, following the original design and acquired some original parts. Work also continues to fit a full set of assister rams and a twin spool valve on the back.

The whole project has not been a solo effort, on at least one occasion it became more than one person could handle. Grahame would like to thank all those individuals and companies, who have helped him to achieve his goal. ∎

The end result! Photo: Peter Love.

Unconventional County

Many will think of County tractors as equal-wheeled monsters designed for pulling huge implements, effortlessly in wide-open fields. The company did, however, produce a number of unequal-size-wheeled machines in the mid-Seventies for use in and around smaller farm yards.

County always recognised there was a market for smaller four-wheel drive models for use in tight yards or on smaller farms where immense traction wasn't necessarily required. So, in 1975, when Ford launched its new range of tractors, County took the 77hp 6600 and 94hp 7700 and offered two unequal-wheel machines for the first time and revised the rest of the range.

Introduced at the Smithfield Show in December 1975, the 6600-Four and 7600-Four filled a gap in the market for a more manoeuvrable and compact four-wheel drive tractor and one of the first machines to be fitted with a quiet cab inline with UK regulations.

Drive to County's own front axle was taken from the rear using a single shaft arrangement to a standard County axle half-shaft as used in the bigger County models. The turning circle was slightly better than the equal-wheeled brothers, but sadly it was still 12.5m – which was an issue.

Powered by Ford's four-cylinder 256DF engine, the 4.2 litre unit was turbocharged

in the larger 7600-Four. The 112mm bore and 107mm stroke of the four-cylinder provided healthy figures of torque between 284Nm and 361Nm at 1,300rpm.

There were no thrills in the gearbox department, 8 forward and 2 reverse speeds, or an optional 16 forward and 4 reverse on the larger of the pair. Ford's Q cab provided a very good operator environment, although there were also a few supplied with Duncan and Lambourn cabs in addition.

More new models

The 6600-Four and 7600-Four were built up till 1981, but were joined in February 1978 with another two models which featured a flat-floor cab. Fitted with a cab built by the Swedish firm Hara, the new 6700-Four and 7700-Four featured the same power of the existing models, but benefited from a flat floor cab which and was painted white following the same livery as the other machines in the range.

However things started to head down-hill when Ford made the decision to produce their own four-wheel drive machines and County couldn't compete on these cheaper export machines in the time of the recession.

Ford opted for the use of ZF axles on their machines since 1978, but also offered Carraro four-wheel drive on their smaller three-cylinder models.

With the introduction of the famous 10 series in October 1981, County offered two economy versions to try and boost sales over the Ford examples. The restyled 6610-Four E and 7610-Four E used a slightly larger turbocharged 4.4 litre engine to obtain 82 and 98 horsepower respectively. Instead of its own axle, County now opted for the Italian-built Carraro to save money and to improve the turning circle to under 11 metres.

The end

With very few models produced, both County and Roadless were struggling to compete with Ford and their new four-wheel drive derivatives. Production ended in 1983 when County concentrated on their equal-wheel machines and the 'Four' became no more. Today many of these models have been exported due to the high demand for simple and easy-fix tractors, and the source of good Ford machines drying out. The 10 Series versions are now particularly rare due to the limited amount produced. ∎

The 7600-Four was launched in 1975 and with the smaller 6600 were County's first attempt at unequal-wheel four-wheel drives.

Without a steam cleaner, various attempts using detergent failed and in the end, the wire brush technique was employed to remove all the grease and muck.

Reconstructing an 1124

Acquired in a terrible 'worked' condition, Howard Sherren's 1968 County 1124 restoration was set to be a real challenge. Requiring many hard-to-find parts, the tractor had a slightly confused identity, but the project gave its new owner the opportunity to gain plenty of experience in the field of restoration. Howard tells the story.

o here it is, the tractor in question, a rather bruised and battered ex-farm 1124 Super-Six which had lay dormant for around five years, prior to purchase in September 2002 from a farm in Bowling Bank near Wrexham, North Wales. Believed to be a 1968 model registered on a Q-plate, its history was somewhat uncertain. Starting life originally in forestry, the County was found by its previous owner in a very poor state in the middle of a wood, and sadly non-operational.

Thought to be pre-Force tractor, the 1124 had the early louvered fibreglass bonnet

with a Ford Force front cowl, which was later found to be from a long-nose Roadless 115 version professionally shortened.

10,000 hours of excellent service
The Duncan cab and round fenders were also fitted by the last owner to ensure that the tractor was usable. With the tractor in a complete but somewhat tatty condition, it was used on clamp duties at silage time on the dairy farm where it completed 10,000 hours or more of excellent service.

After receiving various engine transplants in an attempt to keep this six-cylinder monster going it was, sadly, parked up when it was replaced by a big 4WD American Case in the late-1990s. The last owner was

very sad when he eventually parked the tractor up, as it did such a great job and consolidation was excellent.

After getting the 1124 back home via a tractor and low loader combo, I decided that it would be nice to complete the restoration by the 75th anniversary of the County Commercial Cars Company in 2004, which sadly didn't happen after a number of complications reared their ugly heads.

Grease removal
When the tractor first arrived, it was in a reasonable ex-farm condition but with a very worn engine and coloured a shade of green thanks to mother nature. It drove adequately and was mechanically sound, as the ➡

Right: With the front axle removed from the casting, the true extent of the damage to the pivot pin could be assessed. The bushes were extremely worn and replaced; seals within the stub axles were also changed as substantial leaks stemmed from the input shafts.

previous owner had kept it well greased and maintained. The first job was to remove the layer-upon-layer of built-up dirt and grease. Without a steam cleaner, various attempts using detergent failed and in the end, the

County

1124 specifications

Engine	Ford 2704E
Power (hp)	113
Max power @ (rpm)	2,250
Max pto power (hp)	93
Cylinders	6
Displacement (cc)	6,227
Bore (mm)	107.2
Stroke (mm)	114.9
Fuel capacity (litres)	75.4
Standard transmission	8 forward 2 reverse
Top speed (mph)	21.39
Turning radius (mm)	11,740
Length (mm)	4,090
Width (mm)	2,184
Weight (kg)	4,260
Tyre size	13.6 R38
Produced	1967-71
Cab	Duncan safety

wire brush technique was employed.

Within a few months the original square rear fenders were located from a farm close to the tractor's original location and brought back for a small fee. The parts were in surprisingly good order, considering that they had been left to the elements for many years. I decided to keep the cab intact, so modification was required to make the fenders fit when required.

With help from a local tractor exporter, a set of matching 16.9 R34 wheels and 40% Goodyear tyres replaced the taller, original 13.6 R38 rims. The look-out began for a Super Six bonnet which was eventually found in my local exporter's yard and a swap was made. The tractor slowly began to take shape, before moving onto the next step – the complete strip down.

Replacing worn-out parts
Thanks to gallons of penetrating oil, the tractor was slowly stripped of all its parts to leave the bare casting. This made it easier to split the tractor, to replace worn-out parts and clean each section ready for painting. With the 1124 split into three parts, the front casting, front axle and back-end made preparation and accessibility easier.

The back-end needed very little work as the brakes had recently been replaced. The clutch was relatively new as both were important on silage work. Next, with the front axle removed from the casting, the true extent of the damage to the pivot pin could be assessed. The bushes were extremely worn, but finding replacements wasn't a problem and the pivot could be saved without major financial damage.

The bushes were very simple to slide off and back on again. At £46.73 from A. P. Tavernor of Ludlow they were generally very reasonable and affordable. Seals within the stub axles were also changed at this time, as substantial leaks stemmed from the input shafts. Again, the outlay of £23.40 was cheap enough and fitment was simple thanks to a bolted collar. The Tavernors became extremely useful and were able to source

nearly all the required parts. A big "thank you" to Adrian and Andrew for all their help with the restoration.

Power unit
After the engine was removed, the front casting – the sump could be cleaned up with wire brushes on drills and grinders to get down to the bare metal. It was then subjected to multiple coats of red oxide

Left: The engine was at least the fourth to be installed in the tractor, a replacement in the form of a Ford 'D' Series 380 with a Bosch fuel pump from a friend's truck. A few modifications to the position of the oil filter were required to allow for the extra length of the fuel pump.

was also required, so a badly-rotted unit was found on a breaker for £100 and welded up professionally to solve that problem.

The painting begins

After the engine was in place, each individual part received a thorough cleaning and a few coats of primer, before moving onto multiple top-coats.

This difficult task took a long time, with many parts receiving two coats of blue before being reinstalled. Up to four coats of blue were given to the main casting to remove the imperfections and create a finish that shone, but the process cost a small fortune in paint and thinners.

With the majority of the painting finished, many of the individual items could be refitted before the tractor received its final coat. A pick-up hitch was also sourced from a Ford 5000 to make the tractor that bit more usable.

New arms were fabricated to join up to the County's unusual assistor ram design, another challenge and experience for the intrepid restorer! ➡

primer using a very small compressor and spray gun which took some time. The engine was at least the fourth to be installed in the tractor, so a replacement had to be found which was in the form of a Ford 'D' Series 380 with a Bosche fuel pump from a friend's truck.

The original 2704E industrial engine was hard to come by and the 360 Turbo already fitted was way past its prime. A few

modifications to the position of the oil filter were required to allow for the extra length of the Bosche fuel pump. An exhaust U-bend

The restoration was finally completed in late 2005 and the result was definitely worth the time and hard work that went into it.

Bodywork woes

With most of the tractor in one piece, the engine was fired up. The machine was taken for a spin, and no major problems came to light, so attention turned to the bodywork. The replacement fibreglass bonnet was in slightly better condition than the original, but much work was still required.

A new centre hinge and decal kit were kindly provided again by Adrian Tavernor for the small sums of £25 and £80 respectively.

A number of weeks followed where many hours were spent fibre-glassing and body-filling to obtain a perfect result. The hard work here really paid off and the transformation was amazing. The front cowl received a similar treatment before we fitted a Ford Force metal grill, sourced for £50 from Robert Wraight in Ashford, Kent.

Disappointingly, the County badge was missing, so with the help of Ian Williams at Tractor Panel Ltd, a badge was moulded and manufactured in polished chrome – the mould being based upon a plastic badge from a friend's 1184. This really set the tractor off and our example has helped and inspired many other County enthusiasts to add that finishing touch to their machine.

Nearly there

Wheels and fenders were sent off to be welded and sand-blasted at a local firm in order to save time. Each received numerous coats of paint and were quickly re-fitted. Attention was then turned to the electrics. The wiring loom, running past the engine, was in need of complete replacement but the rest of the system wasn't in too bad a condition.

A new light switch was acquired from Tavernors, again for the tidy sum of £15, which cured the lighting problem, along with side lights and Butler indicators which were found through *Tractor & Machinery* classifieds. A flashing relay took some sourcing, but a standard relay unit from a local automotive store was finally used as a compromise.

Another problem

Sadly, the restoration came to an abrupt halt when the steering failed. Many professionals diagnosed the problem to be dirt in the power-assisted steering ram as it steered in just one direction, so I set about dismantling and cleaning it up. With the steering reassembled the problem still persisted, so a new ram was clearly required. Everyone agreed that further attempts at reconditioning were pointless.

Mike Williams Engineering at Ruthin, North Wales eventually came to the rescue and supplied a brand new ram for an exchange and the sum of £283. This was a shocking expense, but at least I knew it was right.

The problem remained even with this new fitment, so the steering pump pressure was increased. However, the pump couldn't take it and – frustratingly for me – cracked itself in two. Mike Williams Engineering was again a great help and supplied a new pump, this time for £263. This was very easy to swap on the front timing cover and received a little tuning before the steering was eventually sorted out.

The restoration was finally completed in late 2005 and the result was definitely worth the time and hard work that went into it. The tractor is a pleasure to drive and certainly turns a few heads when out and about. Saving the tractor from scrap or possibly export was an achievement and certainly made the project that little bit more worthwhile. ∎

Starting its life in forestry, the 1124 has had a mixed history. Now it has a peaceful life in the rolling Cheshire countryside.

Anywhere and anything

Howard Sherren on the virtues and vices of buying an 1124 second-hand.

With the continuing popularity of Ford and Ford conversions, investment in a County wouldn't be a bad idea. The tractors are becoming harder to find as most are still at work in the woods, have been stripped and the Ford skid unit exported or have found their way into the hands of collectors or enthusiasts.

This buyers' guide looks at the early 1124 Force model, which first saw the light of day in July 1967 when it was introduced as the larger brother to the 1004 in the Super Six range.

Powered by a Ford 2704E engine, from the industrial side it pushed out 113hp. Competition came from the likes of Bray and Doe, with the main competitor being the 115hp 115 model from Roadless.

The 1124 was based on the pre-Force Ford 5000 skid unit and, costing £2,695 when it was launched at 1967's Smithfield Show, was a considerable jump from the likes of the sub-100hp two-wheel drive tractors of the mid-sixties.

With about 2,700 of these models produced in a five-year production run, the model certainly proved popular in the UK and abroad. The 1124 can be remembered for its curvy, fibreglass bonnet and louvred vents on the early models, with the model decals on the nose cone and County badge on the fuel tank.

Later models received a cleaner look with the introduction of the Ford Force models in June 1968, which lost the louvred effect and moved the decals to across the side.

Other improvements saw a Ford 2704C engine fitted from May, 1970, and a 2714E engine fitted from November, 1970 – both still 113hp.

The 1124 was finally superseded by the 1164 in January 1971, which boasted 116hp from a Ford 2000DRT engine unit.

Due to the large export demand for Ford 5000 tractors, many County tractors were stripped to the skid and the parts weighed in, while the skids were exported to Eastern Europe. ➡

Keep a look out for the original burgess exhaust, this Ford 5000 version will be the next best thing.

Also, due to the hard life many were subjected to, it is not unusual to find one tractor made up from bits of others to keep one running. Now many have been snapped up by collectors, there are fewer 'good' examples out there to purchase or even rough examples still out in forestry. We point out problem areas that should be explored if you find a model to purchase.

Engine

The Ford Industrial six-cylinder engine was mounted on a heavy cast sump, which was fixed directly to the transmission with side rails for extra support.

This whole design meant the tractor was rock-solid and increased the weight and therefore improved the traction of the tractor.

The original unit fitted to the 1124 was a 2704E engine which produced 113hp; although the engine model number changed to 2704C, the power remained unchanged until the last tractors from early 1971 gained an extra 3hp.

You can often find the engine model stamped on the side of the engine but, thanks to plentiful supplies, the engines were often swapped instead of being rebuilt, meaning it is a good idea to check it first. By checking the serial plate on the left-hand foot step, a production date can be found and the model of engine it should have can be worked out.

The code can be deciphered as the first number was the year, the second letter the month and the third unit was the day.

A common replacement engine was the Ford D Series 360 or 380, which would normally fit straight in with little or no modification such as swapping the sump, oil pump and strainer across.

Above: The fibreglass bonnet lifted clear to provide access to the Ford 2704E engine. Although this example was fitted with the 380 model, substitutes can be easily found.

Below: The 1124 was introduced in 1967 and was built for five years, with a total of around 2,700 built.

Production

Year from	Year to	Engine	Transmission
July 1967	March 1970	2704E	5000
March 1970	January 1971	2704C	5000
January 1971	July 1971	2714E	5000

Ford 360 and 380 engines can be fitted into the County by swapping the oil pump with the strainer and moving the oil filter location.

1124 specifications

Engine	Ford 2704E
Power (hp)	113
PTO power (hp)	93
Max power @ (rpm)	2,250
Cylinders	6
Displacement (cc)	6,227
Bore (mm)	107.2
Stroke (mm)	114.9
Fuel capacity (litres)	75.4
Top speed (mph)	21.39
Transmission	8 forward 2 reverse
Turning radius (mm)	11,740
Length (mm)	4,090
Width (mm)	2,184
Standard weight (kg)	4,260
Tyre size (front)	13.6 R38
Tyre size (rear)	13.6 R38
Cab	Duncan safety
Production started	July 1967
Production ceased	July 1971

You should check the oil to see if it has been contaminated by water - a good sign it will need replacement - and excessive smoke from the breather pipe is not good news. Check for welding to the sump and around the connection to the bell housing. It is unlikely you will find an engine in complete original condition, but look out for the correct County pre-cleaner as it is highly desirable, as is the original Burgess exhaust.

Gearbox

An up-rated version of Ford's eight-forward and two-reverse gearbox was fitted to County's 1124. Many examples were fitted with heavy-duty bearings, ideal for forestry work, and these could be identified by 'heavy-duty' stamped into the plate on top of the machine. Also this showed that the gear ratios for second and sixth were different.

There was no fancy splitter, just precise gears powered through a 14in heavy-duty clutch. There were options of reduction boxes, which increased the length of the tractor and gave more speed options.

The pre-Force tractors had a starter isolator mounted on top of the transmission, while Force models were conveniently placed inside. Top speed was an impressive 22mph and it was certainly a challenge to keep the tractor on the road when travelling flat-out.

Not much to concern buyers here, just ensure the transmission is what you require.

Rear linkage

The rear linkage was the standard Ford kit, fitted with two assistor rams by County to give it that extra lifting capability. The standard Category II linkage could lift approximately 4,200kg at the lower link balls, which was adequate for most operations.

Many tractors will probably be missing the linkage and just be fitted with a draw bar,

others with just an internal lift cylinder and standard arm, although the assistor rams are definitely worth finding.

Linkage wear will be less of a problem if the machine has been in forestry, but ➡

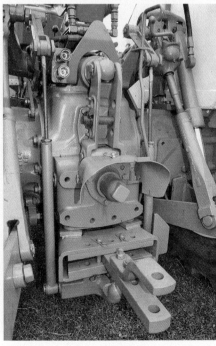

A pick-up hitch is a useful addition from a Ford 5000; look out for these when buying.

agricultural versions should be checked for wear in all the joints and signs of welding around the ball joints, although second-hand and new replacements are readily available. A pick-up hitch from the Ford 5000 could be fitted which improved the tractor's versatility, a draw bar was often standard and bolts should be checked regularly for their tightness.

Hydraulics and pto

A gear pump could originally muster up around 24 litres per minute of output, not particularly good by today's standard but enough for most jobs. One or two double-acting spools could be fitted, something worth looking out for, too.

The power steering had a separate pump and reservoir. The early models were fitted with power-assisted steering (PAS) while later models came with a more reliable hydrostatic unit. PAS systems can be temperamental and a new ram is often required and can be bought for around £290, while the pump is similar at £265 from an aftermarket supplier.

A 1,000rpm pto was a standard fitment offering 93hp, but a 540rpm was available as an option along with a 650rpm version. Look for the speed best suited to your operation and check to see if it stops as a pto rebuild may be an unwanted added expense.

Axles & brakes

County used its own front axles, which consisted of two drive hubs mounted to a solid axle. The drive for these hubs was taken from an output shaft, driven by bevel gears in the rear final drives. To enable the front axle to steer, telescopic prop shafts with universal joints at each end were used to keep drive permanently to the front wheels.

The steering lock suffered due to this arrangement and, with equal-size wheels, increased the turning circle dramatically. Unassisted, 11.7m of space was required to turn the tractor, but this was halved to 5m when the independent brakes were anchored on. For this reason the oil immersed, disc brakes could wear unevenly if too many tight turns were made in one direction only. With four discs per side, the brakes were excellent and lasted ages if regularly adjusted.

Wear is likely to be found in the main pivot, where a lack of grease has caused

The rear linkage could be fitted with twin assistor rams seen here, which boosted lift capacity to around 4 tons.

increased axle movement. Also check for excessive play of the front hubs and steering joints. Driveshaft universal joints can get a lot of grief and wear, but parts are easily found and replaced. The bushes are very simple to slide off and back on again and at £46.73 they are reasonable from AP Tavernor Company in Ludlow.

Seals within the stub axles are also easy to change, thanks to a bolted collar, and at £23.40 are cheap, so are hub seals at £18 and rear drive output seals at £10.50. Check for leaking seals all round, most are easy to change and, if restoring a tractor, they are definitely worth replacing to avoid tears later.

Cab

Although a cab wasn't standard, many 1124s were fitted with a single or double-door Duncan cab. Some early models may have even been fitted with an early Fritzmeier canvas cab, but the Duncan will be considerably easier to get parts for as the company still exists.

Many operators opted to remove the cab as it was a whole lot noisier with it fitted but did provide protection from the harsh elements of the UK.

Rear mudguards were large and square, renowned for rotting out on the inside struts, so check this as replacements are not available. A 30-gallon auxiliary tank may also be fitted to the top of the rear right fender, useful for long working days.

Turning to the bodywork, a new centre hinge can be provided by Adrian Tavernor for £25 and a decal kit for £80. The fibreglass bonnet will often require work as it was vulnerable and not up to the job. An alloy top grille should be fitted and re-manufactured items can now be bought.

If the County badge is missing from your tractor, Ian Williams at Tractor Panels Ltd can provide a remanufactured badge in polished chrome for £30. This can set the tractor off and has helped many County enthusiasts to add that finishing touch to their machine.

Driving

After climbing the steep and narrow step, one has to manoeuvre around the tight lower door frame and centre-mounted gear sticks to get into the driving position. Once seated, you begin to realise that the Duncan cab is not one to spend long hours in, so it is lucky it can be removed when required.

Moderate force is required to use the clutch pedal and the centrally-mounted gear levers move freely and precisely into gear.

Once moving, the tractor's lack of steering soon becomes apparent. If a tight turn is required, the independent brakes could be the quickest way thanks to lack of steering angle and the small delay in assisting ram. Brakes are positive and require little effort.

Power-assisted steering can be temperamental, new rams and pumps are still available at a cost.

The view to the front is somewhat obstructed by the large exhaust, raised air cleaner and bulging bonnet. But, overall it is an exciting drive when you hear the bark from the six cylinders and the immense traction means the tractor rarely slips and it effortlessly pulls up the steepest of banks without a hesitation. The equal wheels certainly give an imposing presence and you get the feeling you can go anywhere, while turning a few heads!

Verdict

Despite the manoeuvrability issues that nearly all equal-wheel Countys have, the 1124 continues to excel in many operations and would be an impressive machine to add to a collection thanks to its unusual curved, fibreglass bonnet.

The 1124's supreme stability and traction ensure that it can go everywhere and do almost anything.

With cracked fibreglass bonnets and rusting wings being the biggest killer of these tractors, high-houred machines still continue to give sterling service.

When the engine is worn, replacement is easy thanks to plentiful supplies of Ford engines from old trucks. Although many County models are becoming hard to find, good original examples can still be found and there might be the odd few still in the hedge or forest.

The majority of tractors will fall into the £4,000-£7,000 bracket. Restored or mint examples may fetch up to £10,000 if they can be found, but in whatever condition a 1124 would make a good investment.

* Thanks to Adrian Tavernor for his help. ∎

Useful contacts

Robb Morgan
County Parts
Craven Arms, Shropshire
01588 672390

A.T. Osborne
County Parts
Romsey, Hants
023 80814340

Adrian Tavernor
County Parts
Ludlow, Shropshire
01584 890276

Jas P Wilson
County forestry conversions and parts
Dumfries
01556 612233

The County gives an imposing presence from the front and at 4,260kg, it weighed considerably more than the others.

Parts availability and how much?

Model	Year from	Year to	Mechanical	Bodywork	N	C	1	2	3
1124	1967	1971	5	3	£2,695	£12,000	£10,000	£6,500	£4,000

(Guide - N: Price when new, C: Concours condition, 1: Excellent condition with no faults, 2: Tidy condition and useable, 3: Rough condition, for restoration or possibly breaking. Parts availability scored out of 5).

Lots of surprises

What started as a simple restoration ends up as a major project, as Howard Sherren finds out.

T he late 1960s County tractors are an unusual sight on today's show and restoration circuit, but there is still love and loyalty for the Hampshire-built brand.

Many feel the Pre-Force and Force models of the 1960s and early 1970s are among the best-looking tractors ever produced. This can definitely be said for the likes of the six-cylinder 954, with its fibreglass bonnet and louvered vents, and then of the 1124 model with its Ford Force styling of smooth and sleek lines.

Simon Priestner's immaculate County 1124 after many hours of hard work.

The tractor looked in a reasonable original condition when it first arrived.

At the peak of their popularity, County tractors were at a premium and there are fewer and fewer good tractors up for grabs. Simon found his in a farming paper in 2006. It was at a machinery dealership in Somerset and looked, at least at first glance, fairly straight and relatively complete for a forestry model.

The history was pretty much unknown. The logbook showed there had been five previous owners, the last being from between Southampton and Bournemouth – probably the area where the dealer bought the machine from a farm sale.

Fitted with a massive winch and the incorrect, later square dish wheel rims, it was likely that the tractor had a hard life in the woods and on the farm.

Bought with a clutch fault, it didn't want to go into gear, although everything else appeared to work – with a bit of play here and there. This was to be expected, given that it had recorded more than 9,000 hours.

However, once Simon got it home, things started to go downhill and the original-looking tractor started to reveal many complicated and expensive issues. A big project was unfolding!

The first job was to get the huge winch removed, which restored some of the steering effect. This was quickly listed on eBay and sold for a healthy £500, which helped towards the next headache – a complete linkage.

The back end was rather bare until an agricultural linkage and assistor rams could be sourced which was capable of lifting 4,200kg. Again the internet auction site was consulted and slowly a complete linkage ➡

This is one of the main reasons Simon Priestner, of Dunham Massey near Altrincham, Cheshire, fell in love with this particular model – "They are something a bit different and the styling is just stunning. Once you have driven one you know how incredible the tractor is and how nothing else comes close, especially for traction."

Finding a good County, and especially an 1124, is no easy task and proved a challenge for Simon compared to locating his other tractors, such as his Ferguson TE-F20.

With the tractor split, the strip-down began. It revealed horror after horror.

One of the best bits of the tractor – the gearbox! This area required no work and was put to one side ready for re-assembly.

was found, along with a pick-up hitch from Roadless dealer, John Bownes.

A simple swap you may think. Yes - if the tractor wasn't so worn. The lower linkage holes were oval and there was considerable play in all the joints, which required hours of machining and bushing; the trumpet housings were removed later on.

When fitting a Ford-style pick-up hitch to a County with assistor rams, many will know that the adaptor arms for the lift rods are extremely hard to come by and will often require fabrication. Simon, however, was lucky enough to have a friend with a host of hard-to-find spares who donated them - things were looking good!

The next logical step was to try to make the tractor driveable – which started with splitting it.

Inside the bell housing everything was plastered in oil, both through the

transmission input seal and rear crank seal: the clutch was worn out and in a very poor state. The splines on the pto driveshaft that goes into the centre of the flywheel were very badly worn, so it was decided to change it, which meant splitting the gearbox from the back axle -which then opened up even more problems in the back end.

The flywheel was skimmed at home and the hub for the pto driveshaft was constructed by welding in a standard Ford unit – a considerable saving.

Whilst split, it was decided that although

the engine ran, it would be daft not to delve into it and check that everything was satisfactory.

The 1124 used a Ford Industrial six-cylinder, 2704E engine that was mounted on a heavy cast sump, which was fixed directly to the transmission with side rails for extra support. This original unit produced a generous 113hp, but the engine model number changed later to 2704C, although the power remained unchanged. In addition, the last tractors from early 1971 gained an extra 3hp.

It is rare to find an 1124 with the original engine, as a common replacement engine was the Ford D Series 360 or 380, which would normally fit straight in with little or no modification such as swapping the sump, oil pump and strainer across.

Thankfully, the original engine was still in place and the head was duly removed - revealing yet more problems that would hit Simon's pocket hard.

It was found that every top piston ring bar one was broken and the general state of the head was rather poor.

The decision was made to pull out all the stops, so the block was put in the capable hands of Steve at Mobile Rebores who machined each cylinder by just ten thou. Then Simon treated each to new rings with pistons, and a new oil pump was installed. The head received new valves, seats, springs, seals and core plugs – nothing was left untouched.

The crankshaft was sent away and re-ground by Park Diesel Services, of Trafford Park, who also sent the fuel pump and injectors away for servicing. They were the bringers of yet more bad news: not only was the rack stuck in the pump, but they deemed it unserviceable.

The fuel pump issue was resolved by Wilkinson's at Stockport after Simon's friend Giles Moston found a pump which could be

The front axle pivot pin was in a sorry state and seriously worn, which again left no other choice but to cut the weld off and replace it.

A replacement front axle support was located.

suitable and Wilkinson's gave it the once-over. With the pump back, the other bits and pieces were re-assembled along with new bearings all round the engine, a new water pump, hoses and hydraulic pipes.

Another friend Lee McBride had the responsibility for sending the radiator away to be checked, again ending in more expense with a re-core. With the engine back together and running smoothly, attention could be turned to the driveline and the rest of the machine.

Once the cab was removed the tractor became more accessible and soon other issues were noticed. The bolts on the steering box had become loose at some stage, which allowed all of it to twist. This caused the dowels to wear over time, meaning they had to be removed, drilled and fitted with larger pins, before the box was re-sealed.

County used its own front axles, which consisted of two drive hubs mounted to a solid axle. The drive for these hubs was taken from an output shaft, driven by bevel gears in the rear final drives. To enable the front axle to steer, telescopic prop shafts with universal joints at each end were used to keep drive to the front wheels – permanently.

The steering lock suffered due to this complicated arrangement and, with equal-size wheels, the turning circle was increased dramatically. Unassisted, 11.7m of space was required to turn the tractor; but this was halved to 5.0m when the independent brakes were anchored on.

The steering didn't seem quite right on Simon's machine and there was little to no power assistance. With the ram off and pulled to bits, it was found that the valve at the end had eaten one of the springs and caused considerable damage; the ball-joint at the other end of the ram was extremely worn.

The block was machined on-site by Steve at Mobile Rebores – impressive work.

The only answer was to bite the bullet and Simon had it done up with a new rod and re-sealed; it had a new steering pump just in case.

It was soon apparent that the front axle had not seen grease for a very long time and was in similarly poor condition to the rest of the tractor.

With the front axle stripped, the main pivot looked beyond repair as it had seriously worn into the casting. This not only needed a new bracket but also the pin was so badly damaged that it required replacing. The weld was ground off and a new pin welded back in place to ensure an as-new finish.

The hubs required new pinions and it was a time-consuming job to sort out the shims and tolerances etc. The four universal joints fitted to the driveshafts added yet more expense.

A heavy-duty version of Ford's eight-forward and two-reverse gearbox was fitted to the 1124. It featured heavy-duty bearings, ideal for forestry work, and could be identified by 'heavy-duty' stamped into the plate on top of the machine.

There was no fancy splitter, just precise gears powered through a 14in heavy-duty clutch. There were options of reduction boxes, which increased the length of the tractor and gave more speed options. The pre-Force tractors had a starter isolator mounted on top of the transmission, while Force models had it conveniently placed inside.

Top speed was 22mph and it was a challenge to keep the tractor on the road at that speed.

There was some good news in the sea of problems: the transmission seemed to be in fine fettle and checking it over revealed no major horrors. ■

With the engine apart, the crank was sent away to be reground and new bearings were fitted throughout.

The wear in the lower linkage pin holes was found to be so bad that machining and bushing was the only option.

Three years of hard work and considerable expense have gone into Simon Priestner's County 1124.

Further challenges

Howard Sherren concludes the story of Simon Priestner's 1124 Super Six.

Simon Priestner fell in love with a County 1124 but when he finally got his hands on it, its restoration just grew and grew as a project. The further he delved into it, the more problems became apparent.

However, the transmission was in good order – but the same couldn't be said for the brakes and pto: with the trumpet housings removed, worn and warped brakes and discs were revealed and the pto clutch was completely worn out – these were replaced.

The back end was re-assembled with new bearings and seals, whilst a new hydraulic pump and rectified idler drive gear were installed.

This gear pump could originally muster up to 24 litres per minute of output, not particularly good by today's standards but enough for most jobs at the time.

One or two double acting spools could be fitted, so Simon ensured he had two

In Chris Collier's spray booth, the 1124 comes together.

16.9 R34 radial, which I think really sets the tractor off with a good depth of tread."

Although a cab wasn't standard on the 1124, many were fitted with a single or double-door Duncan cab. Some early models may have even been fitted with an early Fritzmeier canvas cab, but many operators opted to remove the cab as it increased noise levels and only provided basic shelter from the elements.

Many restorations see the cab banished to the scrap pile but, as Duncan cabs could still provide many of the spares required, Simon had to think twice.

"Many friends and other tractor enthusiasts said I should scrap the cab but I wanted one with a Duncan cab fitted as it suited the tractor. I also thought it would be beneficial, considering the British weather recently."

No parts were left untouched here: new glass and rubbers were fitted all-round, along with a rear window from a John Deere 2130 cab. A new wiper motor and seals finished the tractor off nicely.

The dashboard was re-conditioned by Speedograph Richfield who rebuilt the clock and also reset the hours. Other hard-to-find parts were solved thanks to Mark Osbourne, who located an original exhaust and bonnet hinge among other parts, and Robert Wraight from Kent, who supplied an original Ford Force top grille which was treated to a new reproduction County badge.

Before it was painted, the tractor was run for well over a year after the rebuild (between 2007 and 2008) to ensure everything was working correctly and that the vehicle was leak-free. ➡

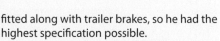

fitted along with trailer brakes, so he had the highest specification possible.

From the outset, he knew there was one major dilemma – the wheels. Getting the tractor right meant that the mint examples of later square dish rims had to go. Four good examples of the correct rims were found at NI Tractor Spares in Lisburn, Northern Ireland, and a swap was done.

As for rubber, there were many hours debating the best direction in which to go. "The tractor should ideally have cross-plys fitted, but this wouldn't be practical for the amount of roadwork I was going to do," explained Simon. "I looked at all brands before eventually deciding on a Firestone

Returning home after painting, all that was needed was the top grille and legendary County badge.

1124 specifications

Engine	Ford 2704E
Power (hp)	113
PTO power (hp)	93
Max power @ (rpm)	2,250
Cylinders	6
Displacement (cc)	6,227
Bore (mm)	107.2
Stroke (mm)	114.9
Fuel capacity (litres)	75.4
Top speed (mph)	21.39
Transmission	8 forward 2 reverse
Turning radius (mm)	11,740
Length (mm)	4,090
Width (mm)	2,184
Standard weight (kg)	4,260
Tyre size (front)	13.6 R38
Tyre size (rear)	13.6 R38
Cab	Duncan safety
Production started	July 1967
Production ceased	July 1971

Above: The Ford 2704E engine received a complete make-over. Each cylinder was bored and received new pistons, rings, bearings and seals. The head received a similarly high standard of treatment.

Top: The linkage was found courtesy of eBay and mostly paid for by selling the winch which the tractor came with.

The front grille came from Robert Wraight after many examples found were deemed unusable.

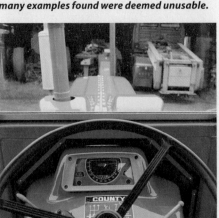

The cab was overhauled, while the dash was reconditioned and the hourmeter reset.

A front weight bracket was neatly extended and a top link bracket added to customise the 1124.

Beautiful paint finish and styling make this 1124 stand out from the crowd.

Above: Perfect in nearly every way. Simon tried his best to return the 1124 to original with a few extras.

Right: The combination of crisp paintwork, Duncan cab, Firestone 16.9 R34 radial tyres and Simon's attention to detail, really make the Super Six a fantastic-looking tractor – one that he should be proud of.

Clocking up 30 hours on working days with a four-furrow plough and running around with the tin work off proved the quality of the restoration as very few leaks or problems re-appeared.

When it came to painting the tractor, Simon decided he hadn't the patience to obtain a perfect finish, which is why he handed the tractor over to Chris Collier of Cavershall near Stoke-on-Trent.

The firm took the complete tractor away and returned it fully-painted and finished. Chris is better known for servicing cars, tractors and 7.5 ton wagons, in addition to carrying out insurance body work repairs, but he used to be an agricultural contractor.

Simon was ecstatic with the finished paint job and the tractor made its debut at 2009's Shrewsbury Steam Rally at Onslow Park; it took four hours to drive it there from home and it went like a dream. Fitted with a Priestner stubble cultivator, the County couldn't be stopped on the working field and it was a treat for Simon to use and show-off three years of hard work. ∎

The joy of automatic

The discovery of a County 1124 former airport tug created interest among enthusiasts. Howard Sherren travelled to Sussex for a test drive.

County tractors are renowned for their tractive performance, so are well suited to tough conditions such as forestry, although many found their way into other industries where they may still be found working for a living.

Airports have required the use of tractor tugs for many years to move aircraft around the site. The tugs must have plenty of power, plenty of weight to achieve traction and take up drive smoothly. In the late sixties, County provided a modified version of its 1124 model to a number of different airports across the UK. Jersey Airport acquired one of these special 1124 models and it provided many years of sterling service.

The tractor was finally retired from frontline service and sold in 2005. Cyril Groombridge heard of the tractor after it was advertised in *Tractor & Machinery* and had it brought back to the mainland. Based in Heathfield, East Sussex, Cyril bought the 1124 as a precaution, should heavy snow occur over the wintertime.

The 1124 was first introduced in 1967 as a replacement for the 954. The tractor received a face-lift in 1968 with the introduction of the Ford Force range of machines. It was fitted with the 2704E engine, an industrial version of their 6-cylinder unit. Rated at 113hp, Ford's diesel engine was a good performer and produced maximum power at 2250 rpm. The 6-litre engine had a 104.8 mm bore moving through a stroke of 114.9 mm.

The fuel tank held just 75.4 litres, not really enough for a full day's work.

The modified 1124 featured a down swept exhaust that kept fumes away from the driver and reduced the tractor's overall height considerably. This made the tractor safer to use around any low winged aircraft.

The tug's downswept exhaust.

The transmission was noticeably the biggest difference between the 1124 tug and the standard machine. This model features a Brockhouse 11F torque converter transmission, which is extremely simple and easy to use. One gear lever enables the driver to select high or low gear, while the second lever gives forward or reverse.

The tractor has no proper clutch, just a pedal to operate a switch to disengage drive. To move the tractor, just select a range gear and then simply push the lever into a direction. The tractor remains still until engine rpm is increased using the foot throttle. The design is exactly the same as an automatic car and gives the versatility of many of the newer continuously variable transmissions.

The tractor isn't fitted with any linkage, just a heavy-duty drawbar on both front and rear. The tractor is weighted heavily with four wheel weights on each wheel and large weights over the rear axle to improve the traction available.

This extra weight gives a maximum tractive effort of 7,673kg, ideal for airport duties. The fenders are also different as they cover both the front and rear wheels to stop possible spray.

This particular 1124, with serial number 22760, has just 2,495 hours on the clock. This may not be genuine as the gauge is broken. The tractor has had a re-spray at some point in its life and has been used by British Midland Services and Aviance Companies.

Climbing up on the back of the tractor is straightforward and the seat access unhindered. The engine fires up without a problem and with very little smoke. The

Technical specification

Power:	113hp
Max power @:	2,250rpm
Max torque @:	1,500rpm
Cylinders:	6
Bore x stroke:	104.8mm x 114.9mm
Displacement:	5,950cc
Fuel capacity:	75.4 litres
Transmission:	Brockhouse torque conv.
Length:	4,090mm
Weight:	2,184mm
Wheelbase:	1,820mm
Standard weight:	4,080kg

high range gear is selected firmly, while the direction lever moves easily into 'forward' gear.

The tractor sits still until the engine rpm is increased when the tractor increases speed very smoothly. Once the revs are reduced the tractor comes to a gradual stop.

Manoeuvrability is poor and the visibility is reduced to the side, thanks to the large fenders, which makes work around buildings awkward. It is believed only a few of these tractors exist with this particular transmission, making it even more special. ■

Below: The simple, but effective, rear end.

Only blue will do

Thomas McParland is the youngest member of the Ford and Fordson Association and a huge County fan, as he tells Chris McCullough.

"I have been interested in tractors for as long as I can remember," says Thomas McParland. "Even though I am only ten years old I have been fascinated with tractors since I was able to recognise one – but it has to be blue in colour."

Thomas loves Fords but in particular the County brand, mainly due to the fact that he actually owns one!

He is the youngest member of the McParland family, who run a herd of Jersey and Holstein cows on their dairy farm at Annacloughmullion in County Armagh, Northern Ireland. His older brother Michael, runs the farm but insists that Thomas is a great help and shares the young lad's interest in tractors. In fact, it was Michael who purchased the County tractor for Thomas almost five years ago.

Thomas explains: "We used to have a County 1474 on the farm, which was sold some time ago. It was this tractor that fuelled my interest in Countys and you can imagine how happy I was when Michael said he was going to buy one for me as a Christmas present.

"It turned out to be a 1969 County 1124 Super-6 which needed a bit of tender loving care.

"Michael virtually started at the front of the tractor and never stopped until he had restored everything between there and the back of the tractor. The end result was amazing and I was very chuffed with it.

"We use her for mixing slurry and ploughing. She never lets us down and, hooked up to a three-furrow reversible plough, has no problem turning the sod and making ready the land for maize production. She also spreads slurry with our 2,250-gallon Abbey tanker with ease."

Not only is Thomas the youngest member of the Ford and Fordson Association, he holds the same title in his local Bessbrook District Vintage Tractor Club and says he thoroughly enjoys his membership.

"I look forward to the meetings with great impatience. The club outings are my favourite though and for me my best-ever outing was to Cooley. That was simply amazing, it was such a buzz to have my County down there. Michael drove the tractor on the day, but I really cannot wait to get my tractor licence so I can get behind the wheel on my own."

Thomas attends St Mary's Primary School in Mullaghbawn but, when it comes to homework, he admits he would rather be reading *Tractor & Machinery* than some textbooks.

Thomas received the County 1124 as a Christmas present from his older brother Michael. Its two main roles on the farm are mixing slurry and ploughing with a Kverneland three-furrow reversible plough.

Thomas says that the Super-6 handles the Kverneland three-furrow reversible plough with ease.

He aspires to be a farmer and follow in the footsteps of his brother, already helping Michael with the cows and calves and loving every minute of it.

But until he is old enough to drive his tractor, Thomas will have to make do with his extensive model tractor collection, which features a fine line-up of County models with a 1474 being the favourite.

He says: "My brother and I have built up this collection over the years but the blue Ford and County models are, without doubt, my favourite. We have set up a scaled-down version of a working farm and I spend many hours driving my model tractors around it."

The McParland farm is not only home to the County 1124, it also runs a 1990 TW-15, which spends most of the time on a feeder wagon as the cows are kept indoors most of the year. There is also a 1983 Ford 4610 which is the farm's dedicated scraper tractor.

Young Thomas certainly has a mind full of information and is a real inspiration to all young tractor enthusiasts, but remember: "If it's not blue, it simply won't do!" ■

Thomas's model collection includes an 1124.

Thomas is counting down the years until he gets his tractor licence.

Stunning – there's no other word to describe it!

County of Cornwall

Roger Hamlin reports on a 30-year love affair.

The first time Guy Manning drove a County tractor was in 1973 when his employer asked him to pick one up from a nearby contractor. He thought: "I could quite get used to having one of these."

Thirty years later he saw a County 1164 that seemed to have been abandoned in a field and, when the owner decided to send it to auction, Guy placed the winning bid.

It was not easy to get the vehicle started, even though it had a good battery, and when it did run the engine was obviously very tired and belched out a fair amount of

smoke, although all pots were firing. The real problem was with the front axle and steering.

Guy started to strip the County down. First off was the rusty old Victor cab; the windows were almost no-existent, there were no rubbers and the roof was tied on with baler twine.

The tractor was in a sorry state when Guy purchased it – the cab alone took six months to restore.

were odd so were replaced and the brakes proved to be completely worn out so were replaced almost entirely.

The front axle was completely worn out with leaking seals in the half-shafts and badly damaged swivel bearings and track rod ends and a worn power steering ram.

By the time he had put all that right, Guy had spent the best part of a year on the project but was finally able to start re-assembly and then completely rewire the tractor.

Meanwhile, Stephen Gill from nearby Menheniot had undertaken the six-month job of refurbishing the cab.

He built a frame, using the remains of what was on the tractor as a template, and then reskinned it. When it was offered up to the tractor it fitted like a glove and a pair of brand new doors off eBay completed its refit.

Now Guy was down to the final touches – a new bonnet was found at Osbornes and a new grille on eBay. A new instrument panel was fitted, so was a new seat (but only ➡

The cab had certainly seen better days...

... so a new frame was constructed...

Once the wheels were off, the engine was lifted out and steam-cleaned before being taken apart. Guy discovered three broken rings in three pots - just for starters.

He had the block bored out and sleeved, new valve guide were put in to replace worn-out ones, the head was skimmed and a new camshaft fitted along with new big ends and a new oil pump. Guy painted the relevant bits of the engine and put it to one side while he started work on the rest of his County.

The transmission was in generally good condition, the hydraulic oil pump was checked, a new clutch plate installed, the flywheel skimmed, the hydraulic lift arms

... and doors bought from eBay were fitted.

The attention to detail is second-to-none.

Right: Twin assister rams provide an extra sense of purpose to an already-imposing tractor. The seat will be replaced by the correct type once Guy has loctaed one.

Below: The County's chrome exhaust silencer and silver bonnet decals really set it apart from other tractors. It's obvious that a great deal of time and attention has been devoted to it.

temporarily until Guy can finds the right County model) and new tyres were supplied from local dealer Geoffrey Harris.

Finally it was time for the project to be unveiled to Guy's wife Sara whose role had been the ordering of parts and tolerating the absence of her husband. When she saw the finished County she agreed it had been worth it. ∎

Ken at the controls of the 1254. Photo: Peter Love.

The forgotten star

Peter Love looks at one of 2009's best restorations of a Ford family member. Ken Cooke's County 1254 is a rare survivor that appears to have spent most of its working life in Northern Ireland.

Newtonards, Co Down is where the Cooke family, headed by brothers Ken and Malcolm operate their heavy engineering business and keep their collection of Countys, Muir Hills, and Roadless tractors which they enjoy putting to work and they can often be seen doing so, occasionally visiting this side of the Irish Sea.

The family originally came from County Tyrone, and at the age of six Ken could plough with a Ford Ferguson outfit. "Don't come home until you have finished the field" his father told him. At the end of the season he was expected to operate the potato lifter as well. Still at that young age, Ken saw his father die tragically on the farm when a TVO drum caught fire and exploded.

After that trauma, the family went to live with relatives in another county. At the age of 14, with Malcolm's assistance, Ken went contracting. To this end, they bought a second-hand FE-35 from the local Massey Ferguson dealer.

'Sold a pup'
After they paid the money they found they had been 'sold a pup' with big end problems and no oil pressure. The totally unsympathetic dealer said: "hard luck". Undeterred, they went to the local DB agents, where there was a totally different attitude. They paid half for a 990 and when they finished all the work the rest was paid off and they became loyal David Brown customers for a while, but it was not to last and general dissatisfaction saw the DB tractors part-exchanged by Eric Johnson for a fleet of second hand Ford 5000s.

Frequent requests for help with repairs to farming equipment led to a change of direction for the family and eventually this became the mainstay of their business, where they provide services that keep them much in demand.

Interesting landing
Meanwhile, there was a tractor collection to maintain. As often happens, there was an element of luck to the acquisition of the 1254. The Cookes went to Somerset for the 2007 Malcolm Beaton County sale. This ➡

The 1254 just after it arrived at the Cooke's fabulous collection. Photo: Malcolm Cooke Jnr.

was probably the largest County sale ever seen, setting a record that's unlikely to be broken. The purpose of the visit was to have a good look at a cabless 1254 import that was on offer, but after close inspection they decided against it.

Not long after the sale John Daniel O'Hare was having some repairs carried out on his combine in the works, when Ken was telling him about the sale and that they were looking for a 1254. John said he thought he knew where there was one – and not far away. Ken was initially doubtful, but John was true to his word and at Katesbridge, in the middle of a field, was a County 1254, in considerably better condition than the one they had viewed in Somerset.

They fitted a new battery and with a little tweaking the 125hp tractor was away! After a road test, the deal was done and it was on its way to Newtownards. It joined Ken's larger 145hp turbocharged 1454 (when new, this was far more popular than the 1254).

The cabless 1254 and 1454 models were first shown at a dealer/press launch day in June 1972 at the 19th century mansion house, Elvetham Hall, Hartley Wintney, Hampshire. For various reasons both machines got stuck, but by the time the press saw them things were back on track.

The public saw them just a few weeks later at the Royal Show, Stoneleigh. Here the County flagship 1454 went down very well, but the smaller 1254 was trailing, as the already-established County 1164 was

a far cheaper option and possibly a better machine. Not many 1254s, possibly fewer than 10, were sold to the home market. The model was withdrawn from sale in 1975.

This particular example went to Gates of Baldock, Bedfordshire on 2 July 1974. How it got to Northern Ireland remains a mystery for the time being, although Cyril Johnson or George Burton have been suggested as possible conduits. The hour clock says 4,500, but Ken feels it has done more than that. It had been looked after to some extent, but had gone a little too far to be left original. It was decided to rebuild the machine to a good rally finish.

Work begins

With the 1254 back in the workshop it was time to strip the cab and panels, much of which would need complete restoration. After the Hara cab was removed all the panels were stripped and the skid unit was placed on a solid structure where the tractor could be worked on.

Raymond McCullock knows Fords through and through and he was asked to work on the mechanicals. He stripped the cylinder head and the sump from the Ford 401 DF 6.6 litre six-cylinder engine, from the skid unit on which the 1254 is based.

Raymond found that the liners and rings needed replacing, but the pistons were serviceable. New big ends were also fitted, but the mains were fine and the oil pump was an essential replacement.

The cylinder head needed re-facing, and new valves were installed on re-cut seats. The water pump was renewed, but the radiator was tested and found to be in excellent order. Hoses were replaced, secured by the correct type of clip. The transmission was basically in good order, but it was checked and re-shimmed and a new clutch fitted.

Right: Cylinder head off and waiting for the new liners to go in. Photo: Malcolm Cooke Jnr.

Above: Nearly there... just one or two things to finish off. Photo: Malcolm Cooke Jnr.

Right: The rear crown and pinion are back in place. The breeze blocks help to position it and nothing else. Photo: Malcolm Cooke Jnr.

The differential was removed so that the sensing cross shaft and links could receive attention. They leaked and didn't tighten up properly. They also needed new seals and bushes. The pto clutch was overhauled, as was the linkage at the back end, where there was probably a legacy of its final work on silaging.

All the oil seals and O-rings were replaced. The heavy-duty County four-wheel drive system was checked. The reduction gear housing was heavy to remove but the Cookes are used to handling this type of machinery. ➡

checked. All the front hubs were good, but the track rod ends required attention.

Luckily the wheels were in very good condition and could be used again after a sandblast and recoat. However, all the electrics had to be renewed as they were past resurrection. As a new loom was not readily available a replica was sourced locally. A Delco Remy alternator replaced the Lucas that had been installed.

The engine's injector equipment was overhauled and was found to be in good order, which was a relief. A new silencer was obtained and the rusted air filter housing was rebuilt. With the rugged dash panel and all the controls in place it was time for a thorough field test. All went well with a temporary fuel drum strapped to the back end. This was when the problems with the brakes and the rear sensing arose.

Finished just in time
Next job was to get the paintwork sorted. There were new wings and the Hara cab, but the work was not finished in time for the tractor's public debut at the very last Mount Stewart working event, where it was used for some light work.

Problems arose
So far, the restoration had been straightforward, but the brakes were a problem that was not revealed until the tractor was re-assembled.

Ford introduced a modification to the caliper during the model's lifetime. With new top plates and shaft modifications the brakes on the Cookes' tractor now work very well indeed.

The front-to-back telescopic driveshafts were resealed and the power steering was

With the Fingal Show, scheduled for July, postponed until Sunday 27 September – due to wet weather – it was decided to take the County 1254 along with the family's Muir-Hill 101 – a tractor driven enthusiastically by Ken's wife Isabella. Both tractors performed superbly.

The cab is to be finished off this winter, now that Ken has been able to acquire an original fibreglass roof section. The restoration has not received the recognition it really deserves. Ken says that on the sledge the turbocharged 1454 can certainly out-pull the 1254, but the difference between them is surprisingly small. ■

Above: The Cookes' County 1454 is good enough to be kept in original condition. Photo: Peter Love.

Main image: On 20 September 2009 at Fingal, County Dublin, Ken had the County 1254 working hard with a six-furrow Kverneland conventional plough behind. Photo: Peter Love.

Below: Work was needed on the lower-link-sensed system. Photo: Malcolm Cooke Jnr.

Push-pull ploughing

Peter Small reports on the activities of the Scottish County Tractor Club and is impressed by a skilfully-operated 4WD County 1454.

The Scottish County Tractor Club has been ever presents at the highly-successful BA Working Weekend held at Lyne of Skene, Aberdeenshire in 2010. This is a working event and the County's always put on a good show working in the fields.

It's great to see the County Tractors in their element, and the quality of the work is very good too.

Aberdeenshire is a region famous for its farming but forestry plays a very important part too and much of the County display revolves round timber. The new 4wd working area at the event was situated next to a wood for the timber boys, with the grass park going under the plough for the farm boys.

The club's marquee run by Secretary Frances Ritchie provided information and merchandise for visitors and valuable sustenance for the many drivers.

Frances' partner Charlie Gray is the Chairman, and in keeping with his leadership role he brought out a display that thrilled the large crowd. An early cut of silage meant that the newly shorn grass could be turned over neatly with no trash needing to be buried. This really helped add a quality edge to the eight furrows being turned by Charlie and his tractor.

Ransomes push-pull

The eight furrows in question were part of a Ransomes Push Pull plough that was operated by his County 1454. These push pull outfits came out in the 1980s and found a keen but small customer base. However, they fell out of favour and now are only really seen at these types of events. No doubt the front units were robbed for the plough metal which makes tracking examples down for preservation very difficult.

In Charlie's case the tractor came first when he bought his 1977 County three years ago. It was sourced from Lincolnshire and carries the registration RAU 822R. With just

5,200 hours on the clock it was in pretty fresh condition when it came.

Despite this, Charlie gave it a good going over and it now looks even better. The result is a very tidy original tractor. The white Hara cab has no signs of the dreaded rust bug the rest of the tin work is very square and in full blue bloom. Even the tyres have that full serviceable quality being the period Kleber radials. Their part-worn state does not compromise the grip at all.

Ploughing ahead

To operate the front pushing plough a front linkage has been fitted, this was previously on a Ford 7740, and prior to fitting was modified by Billy Wilson of Clatt, a man with plenty of experience with front linkages. Following the modifications Billy went on to fit it to the County.

These big County tractors were first released in 1972 and were based on the big Ford 9000 tractors. As the model number suggests the tractor kicks out 145 horse power from its six cylinder engine making

Right: The Ransomes three-furrow TSR 300 FD push plough is lifted out of the ground at the end of another round.

it more than able for the eight furrows assembled at either end.

On the back end is a five-furrow Ransomes TSR 300T that had started as a four-furrow and had worked for a local farmer. This Auto-Reset plough was made into a five when Charlie added another furrow on the end. This was quite an easy operation due the design of the main frame.

Hanging on the front end is a three-furrow TSR 300 FD, again an Auto-Reset model. This plough was originally fitted to a local County 1184 and Charlie would dearly love to know if it is the only three-furrow Auto-Reset example still on the go.

The length overall and between the furrows makes it very tricky to operate. But to watch it working you would think that Charlie did this as his day job. Not so, but never the less, Charlie is very close to farming in blue – being a salesman with local New Holland dealer Ravenhill.

Practice makes perfect

Practice for this style of ploughing comes from many of the working events that Charlie and the club attend throughout the North and North East of Scotland. These include the Strathnairn Farmers Association Daviot Working Day in September and the Club's own working weekend just next door to the BA site in October. This event gives the tractor the chance to really stretch its legs in a long field with a nice slope for good measure.

Right: The Ransomes three-furrow TSR 300 FD push plough is lifted out of the ground at the end of another round.

All this practice has paid off as Charlie made a fine job of ploughing with the rest of the member's fleet following in close succession. Any study of the ploughing was short lived as a multitude of further tractors and cultivators soon had the furrows levelled.

This year the Club was on their metal as keen rivalry was in the air with a trio of Massey Ferguson articulated tractors working in the same field. The club always come up with something special and now with a bit of red rivalry it will be interesting to see what happens in the future! ■

The plot measured to perfection as Charlie finishes his section.

The first 'big' County

At the time early County tractors were always considered some of the 'big' tractors on the market, such as the Super 4 and 6 tractors of the late 1960s. However some of the first prairie-sized machines designed for the biggest fields were the 1254 and 1454 which became the flagship of the County line-up. Howard Sherren takes a look at this heavyweight monster.

Following the launch of the Ford 'Force' 6Y tractors in 1968, County had updated their range to match the Ford styling. The 1124 was the biggest in the range till 1971 when the 116hp 1164 was introduced. Gone were the stylish curves of the Super 6 bonnet in favour for a sloping, straight-cut bonnet of the 1164.

With an increase of just 3bhp, the 1164 wasn't enough for the demands of Britain's arable farmers who wanted more power to handle the larger machinery now available to them.

So in March 1972 the company revealed its latest machines based on Ford's 8000 and 9000 Series skid units. The new models included the 125hp 1254 and the 145hp 1454 which both used a 6.6 litre, six-cylinder Ford engine which was turbocharged in the larger model.

A 112mm bore and 112mm stroke provided impressive figures of 421Nm of torque at 1,400 rpm in the 1254 and 518Nm of torque at 1,600 rpm in the 1454.

The transmission offered was the 16 forward and four reverse speed Dual Power unit, but the backend was strengthened and modified to take the extra weight and power of the machine.

Weighing in at almost 7 tonnes, these big Countys would tread lightly and were built for traction.

When it appeared at the Royal Show in 1972 it created somewhat of a stir with lots of orders immediately from many of the big arable farmers with their wide and power-hungry kit.

Fitted with the Victor cab, it was quite an ugly operator station with big sliding doors which weren't the best design. This cab was improved in July 1974 with the introduction of the Hara Q cab which included a wider cab with better doors, lower noise levels and greater operator comfort.

Stephen and Matthew Haylock's 1454 is graced with the aesthetically-pleasing open operator platform.

Specifications

Model	1254	1454
Engine	Ford 401 DF	Ford 401 DFT
Power (hp)	125	145
Rated speed (rpm)	2,200	2,200
Cylinders	6	6T
Displacement (cc)	6,578	6,578
Torque (Nm)	421	518
Max torque @ (rpm)	1,400	1,600
Bore (mm)	112	112
Stroke (mm)	112	112
Fuel capacity (litres)	163	163
Transmission	12 forward 4 reverse	12 forward 4 reverse
Top speed (kph)	26.5	26.5
Length (mm)	4,030	4,030
Wheelbase (mm)	2,060	2,060
Weight (kg)	6,575	6,894
Tyre size (front)	16.9 R34	18.4 R34
Tyre size (rear)	16.9 R34	18.4 R34

Model dropped

The 1254 was priced at £6,310, and the 1454 £6,770, there wasn't much between the two models. Additionally there wasn't much difference in power between the 125hp 1254 and smaller 116hp 1164 so this smaller model

With 145hp and lots of traction, the 1454 coped well with heavy-draft implements. D. Bishop & son's tractor is using a Nayler 2-leg subsoiler.

was dropped in July 1975.

The 1454 continued and in October of the same year it was revamped using the improved Ford 9600 tractor skid unit.

It was at the 1978 Smithfield Show that County tractors unleashed its next weapon, the 149hp 1474. This machine was a similar size and based on the 9700 model but used Ford's superior Q cab and more stylish tin work of the 9700. Additionally, the longer wheelbase improved stability and safety.

This new flagship model soon became popular and these days is extremely sought after by collectors and enthusiasts alike. ∎

Gear selection was dash mounted. The straight lever controlled the range and the cranked lever switched between the four forward gears and single reverse. Dual Power was via a foot pedal.

The large lever lifted the three-point linkage, while the adjacent levers controlled two remote cyclinders. PTO engagement, flow control and draft also fell easily to the driver's right hand.

Nicola and Hugh Morgan are 'hauled' to church by Hugh's County 964, driven by his son, Eirian.

Four Fords & a wedding

Ford enthusiast Hugh Morgan likes to make the best use of his tractors. His daughter's wedding is a prime example of this, Steve Wright explains.

T radition has it with weddings that the bride should wear something old, something new, something borrowed and something blue. A well kept secret at Nicola and Paul Rees' wedding was that Hugh Morgan, Nicola's father was doing quite well here himself. He might not have been wearing it, but his old blue County 964, played a big part in the wedding.

This was much to the enjoyment of the wedding guests who had no idea that the bride was to arrive on a trailer being towed by this classic tractor. Nicola's brother drove the tractor to the church, with her father driving the married couple to the reception after the ceremony.

Hugh's tractors

A keen Ford man, Hugh owns a County 964, Ford 8210, Ford 7635 and an older Ford 333. The County, a 1976 model, is used for

contracting work and also gets out to local ploughing matches. It took over service from a County 944, which in turn had replaced an earlier County 654. A Fiskars 3-furrow plough is used with the tractor with approximately 175 acres being worked a year. The County is also used for cultivating, rotavating, buckraking and sowing seed.

The trailer which was used for the wedding was home-made, Hugh built it for carrying his JCB 405 Excavator. Going at a maximum speed of around 10mph the

Hugh gets some fresh air driving the County 964 on his surprise 60th birthday charity road run.

bride arrived in one piece and in style at Myddfai Village Church, Brecon Beacons, Wales.

It was Nicola's idea to use the tractor and trailer and this really added a magic touch to the wedding, having her brother drive her and her father to the church. The trailer was secretly decorated the day before and luckily a dry day meant everything went as planned.

Nicola has always had a keen interest in tractors and often takes part in ploughing matches on the old Ford 333.

She also organised, just a month before her wedding, a surprise 60th birthday charity tractor road run for her father. This was with the help of the Llandovery Vintage Club.

A total of 27 tractors turned up for the event. Nicola, and her mother Yvonne, managed to get Hugh away from the farm for the morning and the tractor run started at the local town of Llandovery before making their way back up to the farm.

At the end of the run Hugh was presented with a rather special cake, as you can see from the photo! ■

Bottom left: Nicola's brother Eirian putting the tractor though its paces at a ploughing match.

Bottom right: Nicola at work with the Ford 333.

Below: Hugh and his pride and joy taking centre stage on his birthday cake.

The County 1174 with timber-handling equipment is a very businesslike looking machine. It has a front mounted blade for pushing timber and an extremely powerful crane for loading purposes.

Down in the woods

Andrew Hall came across this businesslike County 1174 complete with timber handing crane, blade and rear mounted winch in woods near Leigh in Kent and had to find out more about it.

This particular tractor is owned by Zak Price of Pembury and is in regular use clearing and loading timber coppiced in West Kent. He was somewhat surprised at my interest in the tractor, as he considers it personally to be a workhorse for his trade.

County tractors are naturally highly sought after within the collector's world, but there are clearly still many around in regular use commercially.

The 1174 model was introduced by County in April 1977 and production ran until July 1979. Powered by a six cylinder 113 horsepower Ford engine from the Ford 8700 tractor, the transmission was from the 7600 and featured dual-power with the gear levers at the right hand side. The cab is a Swedish Hara safety cab which was a common fitment at the time.

A side view of the tractor showing the hydraulic oil tank at the front, which acts as ballast when the crane is in full swing. Cast Iron wheel weights are fitted to the rear wheels, which assist in stability as well as traction aids!

Below: The trailer has low-pressure tyres and suspension to cope with rough terrain. The timber on the trailer is Silver Birch, but most within this area is Chestnut.

In addition to the safety cab the crane has a very robust support frame fixed to the rear axle. Tucked neatly into the rear of the tractor is the twin drum winch for coaxing timber from awkward situations! ■

Dressed for work

Roger Hamlin finds an 1174 that has to earn its keep despite its good looks.

Not many people would choose to fully restore a 1977 County 1174 then put it to work hauling logs out of a 20-acre wood. But Rob Tamblin did.

The tractor lives on a farm at Duloe, just outside Liskeard in Cornwall, which has been in his family since 1850.

Rob moved there in April 2007 taking with him a few of his Fordson Major tractors.

Over previous years a few County tractors had passed through his hands, like a 764 with a Boughton winch, an 1184 that also had a winch and a 654. He had restored them all but the County he really wanted was an 1174 like the five he often watched at work on a neighbouring farm.

In March 2008 he was looking in a local farming magazine when he spied an advertisement for a 1977 model. Rob called the man only to be told the County had gone but that he had another one that had been parked up behind a shed for a long time. Rob bought it.

It was delivered to Cornwall but Rob had to drive it several miles home. There was not much power, it was smoking like a chimney, it looked really rough with no doors or back window, the engine was breathing a lot from the breather, the dual power did not work, the tyres were finished and there was no linkage on the back.

It took Rob no time at all to start stripping it down: it would take slightly longer to finish

the task because he could only work on it in the evenings and weekends as he still had a full-time job.

He removed the remains of the rusty old cab, split the tractor to sort out the dual power and then started stripping down the Ford 8700 six-cylinder engine.

Rob had decided he wanted a first-class job done on this his dream tractor and because he did not have a lot of time on his hands, he enlisted the services of Peter Crabb.

The tractor and all the parts were loaded on to

a lorry in May last year and taken to Peter's yard in the nearby village of Dobwalls.

Peter was conversant with County tractors; his father used to run them and whenever he had a chance Peter also drove them and fixed them up when work was required.

He started work by putting the engine back together – new pistons, liners, gaskets were put in, the crankshaft was OK. The transmission appeared to be in good order so he thought it best to leave it alone.

The dual power rods on the floor of the County had been broken, one of the clutch packs was worn so this was replaced, as was the new linkage.

When both ends of the tractor were reunited, Peter talked to Rob about giving it a run before anything else was done, just to make sure all was working well.

They agreed it would be pointless to paint it all up then find a problem this is what they did and it ran like clockwork.

Next on the agenda was the tin work. The nose cone was in an awful mess with holes all over it. Metal was cut, soldered in, then ground down to get the required finish.

The bonnet had been smashed in one corner and it took two days of solid work to rebuild it. Then it was time for the primer and at the end of October the undercoat went on.

Four top coats followed, then the transfers and new lights. The tractor only had to have the seat retrimmed and the interior of the cab done.

Peter had the job all finished at the beginning of November and Rob gave me a call to see it, before it went off to the forest to earn its keep.

Working alongside the County in the woods are a Ford 4610, built in 1984 and fitted with an Igland double-drum winch for pulling out timber, and a County 4600. ∎

This great-looking County 1174 was just finished when the photo was taken. Now it is at work.

Stephen Mageean's magnificent County 1174.

Restoring an 1174

This 1174 was the first tractor purchased by enthusiast Stephen Mageean, from County Down, Northern Ireland. While it was bought to work, it was the subject of an unexpected restoration. Steve Wright finds out why.

Stephen found the tractor for sale in Waterford, in the Republic of Ireland back in 1999. At this time there was not such a big collectors market for these heavy classic tractors, and prices were substantially lower than they are today. In this regard, the timing of the purchase was excellent. The previous owner had used it as a working tractor for the previous seven years but had decided that something more modern would now be more appropriate.

Over this seven-year period it had only been used to pull a silage harvester and a slurry tanker, and while it came with its

hydraulic link arms, these had been removed as they were in effect redundant. Stephen was particularly drawn to the tractor's purposeful appearance and flat-deck cab.

One of the front tyres had suffered a puncture while powering the silage harvester. The hours recorded showed 6,000, but this had stopped counting at some stage, and while the tractor looked it good shape, it was hard to tell what the true hours worked could have been. In the end a purchase was inevitable and the only question remaining was how to get the big beast the 270 miles back home.

Stephen's father John decided that the best option would be to drive it back, and he duly volunteered to do this himself. The

puncture was repaired on the front wheel reasonably quickly and they were soon ready to be on their way.

With the tractor recording a top speed of around 30mph the journey could have taken approximately 12 hours. However it was not exactly plain sailing. The plan was to drive 120 miles to Dublin (just under the half-way point), if they got to Dublin in good time they would then drive all the way home into the early hours of the morning.

Disaster in Dublin
On reaching Dublin the tractor slowed to a crawl, as if it were stuck in first gear. John tried every gear, including the high-low box and Dual Power. Nothing worked and it was

starting to get late. They began to fear the worst, that the Dual Power clutch pack had failed and this was going to be an expensive repair.

They found a haulage yard where they could leave the tractor while they looked into getting it fixed. Having discovered that the most likely problem was that the hydraulic pump had packed up, transport was arranged via low loader to a tractor mechanic in County Meath.

A replacement pump was fitted, and with a very favourable exchange rate four new tyres were also fitted. When the tractor was ready for collection they drove down again and by the time they got home, what could have been a 12-hour journey had in fact taken nearly three weeks!

In 2002 the tractor quite happily completed a 150-mile round trip to take part in the famous Cooley Rally in Co Louth, Republic of Ireland. At this time Stephen's brother was building a house and the tractor was being used with a 12-ton dump truck, something it handled with ease.

Stephen had no intentions of restoring the 1174. However, while on a journey to pick up a trailer, he slowed down approaching a set

The only way to do the job properly is to restore the Hara cab off the tractor, before refitting.

of crossroads and instead of changing down a gear he selected reverse. The net result was a broken selector fork in the gearbox.

Restoration
Unfortunately, the tractor would have to be split to remove and replace the broken ➡

Beginning to look the part again, but still a lot of work to be done.

The cab, complete with new mudguards and a re-spray being lifted to be put back on the tractor.

The tractor ready for splitting to have the broken selector fork replaced.

The business end ready for work and the cab finished with lights and decals.

selector fork. This could have been done without taking the cab off, but after a bit of hard thinking Stephen and John decided to go all the way and restore the tractor.

The restoration was mostly a cosmetic job, as, apart from adjusting the tappets, the engine was in fine condition. Both the clutch and brakes needed replacing, and this was done by the local New Holland dealer, Kennedy's of Ballynahinch. With not a lot of tread left of the tyres it was decided that they should be replaced, so a new set were fitted as were the hydraulic and steering hoses.

The cab was removed with the help of a telescoping loader and the old mudguards were cut off with new ones being sourced from A.P. Tavenor of Shropshire. The cab doors were too far gone and replacements were fabricated. For convenience, the cab was sprayed while still off the tractor, here the assistance of local car body painter John Johnson was required.

The cab was carefully re-fitted, and after connecting all of the linkages the 1174 was taken for a test drive. Thankfully everything worked! The tractor has since twice been to the Northern Ireland County working days, both times with a four-furrow plough which it handles without effort.

The 1174 is now seen on local road runs and at vintage rally displays. Stephen is also keen to take her to shows where bigger tractors can stretch their legs a bit! ∎

Testing the tractor out with the plough, no problems!

Spreading it about

Peter Squires finds Countys being used to fertilise a county's fields.

Sherwood Lime and Sherwood Spreaders have worked together for 25 years around Hodthorpe in Nottinghamshire.

Colin Taylor, who confesses to being semi-retired as head of Sherwood Lime (his son David has taken over), explains: "My company gets the orders and purchases the products to be spread on the land and Sherwood Spreaders is contracted to us to actually spread it."

That company is owned by Eon Heath and Alan Whall, who bought it from Baseley Agricultural.

Eon recalls: "We had three FC Countys then, all bought new - one FC 1004 and two FC 1174s. The FC 1004 went to Jasper Wilson up in Dumfries, Scotland, and another FC 1174 was bought to complete the fleet. We now have three FC 1174s, which works perfectly for our business.

"We bought the basic FC 1174 County as a skid unit with a single spacer box, then bought a McConnell PA44 power arm grab

(minus legs) and an Atkinson body, as used on highway gritting lorries.

"We fabricated a 'bridge link' for the grab to bolt to the County body behind the cab and the exhaust was re-routed to enable the body to fit the County's chassis. The complete machine (empty) weighs around seven-and-a-half tons.

"The third FC 1174 (AAP 590T) was bought as a grey skid unit from a Mr Jones in Aberystwyth. A new chassis was made for it, plus the hopper body as that was dented. To date everything on the machines is totally ➡

Note the extra diesel tank for white diesel.

original. The hopper bodies are lined with wear plates to reduce wear on the body itself from the materials used during operations."

Every year each spreader receives a full stripdown. The hopper body, grab and conveyor are removed with the wheels until the Countys are back to a basic skid unit. New filters are fitted, the fuel tanks are steam-cleaned inside and the injectors are removed, checked and returned with a little copper grease. Sitting on top of the engine casing, the injector bolts get covered in all the sand, salt and fertiliser being spread, so a yearly clean and check are well worth carrying out. The main checks are on the front axle, all bearings, seals and kingpins. The County is then given a full steam-clean before being repainted and put back together.

Eon said: "They are very little trouble. You have to know where you can buy certain parts from, but we have built up a good list of contacts over the years.

"We did look at other models for the basic chassis - Volvo looked good but the price went with the name. For the money County was right, and the tractors have proved very reliable with low maintenance ever since.

Left: Inside the County's cockpit.

Centre: The spreader drive is taken off the pto shaft.

Bottom: Alan uses the door-mounted controls to load up.

"When we bought them new they came as a chassis with a flat top, spacer box and 'forestry' wheels. They were solid with no adjustment, the solid centres having no adjustment.

"The tyres are Michelin Bib'X 18.4 R30, which are fantastic and the only tyres I will have for the Countys."

I went to find Alan Whall, who was awaiting a delivery of lime, and we looked round his FC 1174, which was different in that it had two spacer boxes fitted, giving an extra eight inches to the axle centres.

He said: "These machines do a lot better than a tractor and trailer. They'll turn on 12 metre tramlines in the field – the 4WD prop shafts limit the degree of turn, but that is plenty for the job they perform. They are very manoeuvrable and will go up some of the steepest hills imaginable. I chicken out before the County does.

"Another positive thing is that I don't need to get out of the cab at all. The grab controls are situated inside the cab, so I just drive up to the heap of lime, load up and spread until I'm empty, returning to the heap to refill."

All three Countys are fitted with a ➡

Sherwood Spreaders fleet details

Registration	Model	Serial no.	Engine no.	Code
BBC 839T	FC 1174	39297	338288	78 L 28
CAU 954T	FC 1174	39584	344734	79 B 14
AAP 590T	FC 1174	39006	323701	78 J 25

Speeds achievable

Gear	Speed (mph)
1st	2.1
2nd	2.6
3rd	4.5
4th	6.2
5th	7.4
6th	9.2
7th	16.0
8th	22.2

Reverse: 3.0 (low), 10.6 (high)

Speeds at 3,000rpm with 13.6-12x38 tyres

Every part of the Countys gets steam-cleaned annually.

towing bracket and a white diesel tank. "This enables us to tow our Ford Escort service van behind the County, running on white diesel on the roads, switching over to red when working the field. If we are working a fair distance from base we can leave the spreader at the local farm and drive home in the service van."

Soon Bob Chapman turned up in a Foden and tipped around 20 tonnes of lime. Alan fired up the County and moved beside the heap.

The hopper holds around 4.5 to 5 tons and a conveyor belt below it moves the load to be spread through an adjustable gate, raised or lowered by hand to the required tonnage per acre. The load then trickles down on to two rotating discs, which disperse it on to the field in an even spray. Both the conveyor and rotating discs are worked off the County's pto shaft via belts which drive smaller gearboxes. In minutes Alan had loaded up, and moved into the field to start spreading.

Staff at Sherwood Spreaders don't just work, build and maintain their trio of FC 1174 Countys. Eon explained: "We have built three other models for companies; an FC 1174 for Caister Lime and two (an FC 1004 and a FC 1174) for Steetley."

He was converting a small Nissan pick-up truck into a tipper when I visited the premises and said: "Most of the work is with the Countys but as a result of converting

them into spreaders, we do get a small amount of additional fabrication work."

Lime isn't the only material spread by the Countys. One of Colin Taylor's archive photographs shows an FC 1004 County spreading sand at Sheffield Wednesday football ground and fibre sand was spread on the racecourse at Southwell, Nottinghamshire, when it first became an all-weather racetrack. ∎

Spreading on Sheffield Wednesday's Hillsborough ground in June 1974.

The County at rest in Redesdale Forest, near Catcleugh reservoir, Northumberland, with leaking backhoe slew ram.

Definitely one of a kind

Norman Chapman recalls working with a unique County.

When I first saw the County 1184 I knew it was unique with some unlikely attachments fitted, the main one being a backhoe assembly, the same type as that fitted to Ford 550 excavators.

The County was originally purchased by the North Eastern Electricity Board (NEEB) for a special role - to be involved in the part-refurbishment part-new construction of an Overhead Line Network (OHLN) which stretched from Spadeadam in Cumbria to Kielder in Northumberland.

Most of the terrain consisted of marshy moorland, which proved difficult when it came to planting OHL poles. The year was 1982 and this is when the story begins.

When the Spadeadam job began, the company used Ford 550 excavators, but these soon got bogged down in the soft ground. To try to stop them sinking the backhoe stabiliser feet were fitted with shortened railway sleepers. It seemed a good idea in terms of spreading the weight but the modification was not that successful.

To give an indication of how soft the ground was, poles would be planted one day and the next they would have either sunk, or the top would be the only part visible.

In the many places where this happened, extra work was done preparing the pole. The pole hole was dug wider than normal and a shorter length of pole was fixed horizontally to the base of the vertical pole to give extra stability.

The regular task of recovering bogged-down 550s by Land Rover with winch and/or a Bedford ML with winch proved very time-consuming so extra anti-sinking measures were taken in the form of doubling all of the wheels and tyres on the 550 to increase ground coverage.

The downside to this was the extra strain on the front axle, which caused kingpins to break. This proved to be another quick fix which did not work that well as the 550 was rear-wheel drive only.

Meanwhile, back at the ranch, talks were going on about 'How the hell will we get this job done?' and 'Who else would have a problem like this?' Someone talked to The Forestry Commission, which had tractors

working in similar terrain, and their vehicle of choice was the Ford/County tractor.

It was a powerful, go anywhere, all-wheel drive vehicle which had loads of ground clearance. So the Transport Management department set to work to obtain approval for purchasing a vehicle which would be able to complete the work.

The County was bought from a dealer in Ireland (specifics unknown) and shipped over to England. A local plant dealer fitted a second-hand Ford 550 backhoe assembly to the rear transmission of the vehicle on a makeshift sub-frame. To complete the vehicle at this stage, front weights were added to balance the bulk of the backhoe.

We took delivery of the tractor and, before going on the road, a little extra work was carried out on it at our depot garage. This included fitting flashing beacons, company signs/notices and registration plates A240 ATN. Now the County was ready for action.

It was to be based at the NEEB depot nearest to the Spadeadam/Kielder job, which was in Hexham, Northumberland. It was driven from Hexham to Spadeadam and parked in a secure compound overnight. ➡

Backhoe ram now repaired, the tractor is ready to resume digging the trench through the forest for co-axial cable. The A68 can be clearly seen.

So now, down to work. The first thing the driver/operator noticed was the pungent smell of hot hydraulic oil. A few days of use saw a number of burst hoses to the backhoe. Their renewal wasn't a simple task, purely and simply because of the geography.

Most of the hoses were genuine Ford parts and sourcing them was time consuming. When a hose burst, the fitter had to load his van with tools and two five-gallon drums of hydraulic oil then drive to the vehicle. When there, he would remove the burst hose and travel to a Ford tractor dealer in the shires around Hexham who carried stock. Then he would travel back to the tractor, fit the hose, fill the tank with hydraulic oil and test the operation. All in all, this activity could take half a shift or more to do. So, as hoses were failing regularly, a rethink was in order.

As mentioned, most of the hoses were genuine OE parts so it was decided to purchase a full set for stock. As hoses would fail with regularity, it was time to have the hydraulic system pressure-tested, which discovered it was working over pressure,

hence the hot smell of the oil. So a beefed-up, higher capacity pump was fitted.

Remember, the backhoe was a unique fitment and problems which occurred had to be tackled one by one. It was a case of 'into the unknown to see what's at the other side.'

The job was progressing reasonably well until... the backhoe decided it didn't want any more punishment and shifted from its moorings, taking half the back axle with it.

Job stopped. Heads scratched, 'oh gawd' muttered a few times, the driver was asked if he had noticed anything loose.
He hadn't.

Time for another re-think.

It had been indicated that the tractor would 'flex' when using the backhoe and the balance weights and the rear stabilisers were not that effective. This was purely and simply because of the terrain.

The tractor was made safe by removal of the backhoe, sub-frame and various bits of broken aluminium and then taken by low loader to an agricultural engineer in Swainby, North Yorkshire, for modifications.

The County was away quite a long time but when it came back it had been transformed.

Along each side, a full length sub-chassis had been fitted. Attached at the front was a twin hydraulic ram-operated dozer blade. This had been fitted as a front anchor and, when sunk into the ground, would stop the tractor from flexing. Where the balance weights used to be was now a heavy-duty Boughton hydraulic winch. Directly in front of this, a rope roller had been fitted to the top edge of the dozer blade. At the rear of the County was where the bulk of the modifications had been carried out.

A few years earlier the Ford Construction Company had brought out a new excavator model, the 555 which was fitted with all sorts of innovations. The company had made leaps and bounds and completely restyled the backhoe assembly. New features included a centre pivot operation instead of the old sideshift type. Another innovation was the design of the stabiliser legs. These now swung from the bottom of the backhoe

Rear view, showing new Rotaclaw bucket and the specially made rear light bar. The County did a lot of road miles with NEEB.

The Easter holidays of this particular year were approaching and the job would stop. The tractor would have to be driven back to Swainby for extra wheel modifications – a three-day road journey. I remember the driver's comment: "What a soul-destroying trip, 19mph top speed and when it 'seesaws' it takes some controlling."

Anyway, the wheel modifications were done and I was sent along with one of the company crane wagons to pick up the four extra wheels/tyres. The wagon driver would load the wheels and I would drive the tractor from Swainby to Gateshead. My colleague was right; it was soul-destroying and, when the tractor started to 'whip,' there was very little that could be done. The hydraulic damped seat and the radio were a godsend.

The County went back to work and the Spadeadam-Kielder job was finally completed without any more major problems.

The tractor was now semi-retired and was parked in the depot yard for long periods. There had been a lot of money spent on it originally, and then again on all of the extra modifications, so seeing the vehicle doing nothing was not good. I don't know every job the vehicle was sent on but I do remember the ones I was involved with.

It was unknown for a company like NEEB to do work for anybody but themselves, but times were changing. We had specialist kit, the County being a prime example, and there was an outside contract in the offing which would entail digging a trench and laying heavy-duty co-axial cable through the Redesdale Forest from a telecommunications mast near Catcleugh Reservoir to Byrness. ➡

assembly instead of being mounted on the side of the earlier model. The County was now fitted with the new-style Ford 555 backhoe.

I had noticed the old 550 backhoe on the County did not have much ground clearance: this was obviously dictated by the massive wheels. The original fitment of the 550 backhoe had to be low-slung in order for the stabiliser legs to be able to work. The new, cutting-edge design of the 555 backhoe meant it could be mounted higher and there was plenty of scope for the legs to work effectively.

The terrain at the Spadeadam job had become a bit friendlier and during the County's absence work was proceeding slowly. There were two or three phases to go before the job was finished so the County headed back. Then the going got soft again and the tractor would sometimes find itself bogged down. It was decided that, just like the 550 beforehand, the doubling up of the wheels for extra ground coverage was required.

Front view of the tractor showing dozer blade and Boughton winch.

Left: Do you think we will get the beast on to the trailer? The County on its way to auction.

Below: The tractor, complete with backhoe, is loaded to go to auction.

There were lots of jobs where old OHL network poles had to be replaced. In practice, the County would dig the hole as the linesmen were 'dressing' the pole with metal work and conductors. Then, turning the Rotaclaw bucket, the pole could be grabbed about halfway up and placed in the hole.

In the last year of its employment with Northern Electric (same company, new name) the six-cylinder engine's aluminium sump developed a hairline crack and was removed, welded and refitted.

About a month later the selfsame thing happened again so I took a tip from the Forestry Commission and welded strengthening fillets to the sump at the bell housing side.

Other extra work was carried out on the sub-frame in this same area and this beefing-up work cured the problem.

The County remained with the company until around 1996, during which time little had been done to it mechanically. I know for a fact that there was never a spanner laid on the Ford 401S engine but it did have a new clutch and a couple of power steering pumps fitted.

The tractor was finally sent to auction and sold to a collector in Northumberland, where it is still alive and well. ∎

On one occasion the County broke down and I was called out to it in the forest just off the A68 above the small village of Byrness, near Otterburn, Northumberland. It had a hydraulic oil leak on the backhoe. We were told by the driver beforehand that one of the slew rams on the centre pivot arm was leaking.

When I got to the tractor and checked the leak I decided that new ram seals would cure it. After removing the ram we had to carry it back to the van which was a fair distance away down forest tracks. This ram, although short and squat, was very heavy so we made a sort of stretcher out of pieces of a wooden pallet.

We travelled back to Hexham and did the repair and, apart from the odd hydraulic pipe failing, the work through the forest went well. After it finished the County was again parked up for months.

As time went on all sorts of hydraulic innovations were developed by different engineers. One of these was the Mason Rotaclaw bucket, which could dig holes and also turn 360 degrees.

There was a requirement for this new fangled attachment to be fitted to the County so the tractor had to be driven to Swainby again to the agricultural engineer.

A separate hydraulic system was added to operate the Rotaclaw, and also a system warning device called Liftwatch, an electronic circuit added to the hydraulic system to protect against overloading.

Buyer's guide: 1184

The mid-range 1184 model, produced for just over 10 years, was one of the last models to make it into the Nineties, says Howard Sherren.

Introduced in July 1979, the 1184 TW was the replacement for the existing 1174 model. Surprisingly the 1174 only had a two year production run, which was relatively short compared to the 1184's 11 year victory.

The 1184 featured a new square bonnet which was vastly different to the futuristic, slopeing bonnet style of the outgoing model.

The cab remained the same Hara-built unit, but engine power was increased by 8hp to 120hp by using a new motor. Originally

the 1184 used the power lump from a Ford TW-10, but this was changed two years later in 1981 for the TW-15 item when Ford revamped the TW range.

The production of the 1184 continued when the company was purchased by the Benson Group in 1987 and relocated to Knighton, Powys.

Towards the end of production in 1990, a number of tractors were painted Benson's own red colour scheme and received an updated cab, which dramatically changed the appearance of the tractor.

Engine

The 6-cylinder, 120hp TW-10 engine with its 6.5 litre capacity gave good performance when required. Producing its 120hp maximum power at 2,300 rpm, the Ford power lump also produced the smoke to match. This became a common characteristic of these Ford engines, but was nothing to worry about.

The bore of 111.8mm was slightly more and the stroke of 111.8mm was slightly less than the competition, but it performed as well as or if not better. ➡

1184 models are another popular machine and made it through to the end of production.

County 1184TW

County

The 1184 boasted 120 horses from a Ford TW-10 motor.

1184 specifications

Power (hp)	120
Max power @ (rpm)	2,300
Max torque @ (rpm)	1,600
Cylinders	6
Displacement (cc)	6,578
Bore (mm)	111.8
Stroke (mm)	111.8
Fuel capacity (litres)	139.5
Standard transmission	Dual Power 16 forward 4 reverse
Lift capacity (kg)	4,220
Turning radius (mm)	11,000
Length (mm)	4,080
Width (mm)	2,830
Weight (kg)	5,247
Tyre size (front)	16.9 R34
Tyre size (rear)	16.9 R34
Cab	Hara

With typical, routine maintenance these engines can easily reach in excess of 8,000 hours, before the internals have to be dealt with.

Engine parts are readily available, thanks to the fact that the engine is the same as the TW-10 and TW-15. The fuel tank capacity gave space for just under 140 litres, not bad but could have been a bit bigger for those heavy going operations.

Transmission
The transmission used in the 1184 was a Dual Power gearbox from a Ford 7600. Robust in construction, the gearbox was capable of handling the power after being strengthened. Providing 16 forward and 4 reverse speeds from a five position, dual range, Dual Power synchromesh gearbox.

These were accessed using a gear and range lever with a Dual Power pedal on the floor. The Dual Power feature enabled each of the 8 forward gears to be split. By reducing the power and the speed by 22%, the torque was increased by 22%.

Surprisingly the top speed of this tractor was 22.69 mph, which was nearly 40kph, adequate for a tractor which wasn't easily manoeuvrable.

Drive from the engine was transmitted through a single plate, 14"dry clutch. Both clutch and gearbox are usually trouble free.

Rear linkage, hydraulics & pto
The rear linkage is the standard Ford kit, fitted with two assistor rams by County to give it that extra lifting capability. The standard category two linkage could lift approximately 4,200kg at the lower link

History

1979 (July)	120 hp 1184 replaces existing 113hp 1174 model.
1981	Ford TW-15 engine used instead of TW-10.
1987	County Commercial Cars Ltd bought by Benson Group and production moved to Knighton, Powys.
1989	Handful of 1184s finished in Benson Group Red.
1990	Production of County tractors ceased.

With twin assistor rams the rear linkage produced 4,200kg of lifting power.

balls, adequate for most operations.

There is very little to go wrong here; just check for too much wear in the joints and drop arms.

Again the hydraulics are typical of a 1980s Ford, draught and position controls are used to operate the linkage, with a double-acting top-link control for implement draught. 35 litres/min hydraulic output is obtained at 2,100 rpm from gear pump in the rear of the transmission housing.

Originally the 1184 was fitted with a single-speed 1,000 rpm power take-off, which produced a maximum of 105hp at 2300 rpm. An optional 100hp, 540 rpm speed was available as well, but a dual speed PTO became standard on the later tractors.

Axles & brakes

County used their own front axles, which consisted to two drive hubs mounted to a solid axle. The drive for these hubs was taken from an output shaft, driven by bevel gears in the rear final drives. To enable the front axle to steer, telescopic prop shafts with universal joints at each end were used to permanently keep drive to the front wheels.

The steering lock suffered due to this arrangement and with equal size wheels increased the turning circle dramatically. Unassisted, 11.0m of space was required to turn the tractor, but this was halved to 5.0m when the independent brakes were anchored on. For this reason the oil immersed, disc brakes could wear unevenly if too many tight turns were made in one direction only.

With four discs per side, the brakes were excellent and lasted ages if regularly adjusted. Wear is almost likely to be found in the main pivot, where a lack of grease has caused increased axle movement. Also check for excessive play of the front hubs and steering joints. Drive shaft universal joints can get a lot of grief and wear, but parts are easily found and replaced.

Cab

A challenge is apparent, when attempting to enter the cab. Narrow steps are a result of using equal size wheels, which gave a difficult entry and exit. The doors opened towards the front which added to the hindered access.

Fitted with Hara's quiet cab, the 1184 feature many luxuries as standard, which many others didn't. A flat floor, front and rear wipers with washers, tinted glass, luxury torsion bar suspension seat, three speed heater and a radio. Large front and side windows gave an excellent view all around the tractor, but the view forwards was limited by the straight, square bonnet, unlike the outgoing 1174.

The dashboard was cluttered with an array of buttons and switches, including the radio. Centre was the renowned Ford

Later tractor received the Hara cab seen here, unfortunately sourcing cabs became the demise of County Tractors.

information centre, featuring the vital engine RPM, temperature and fuel gauges. The dashboard also featured an adjustable steering wheel, useful to achieve a perfect driving position.

Gear, spool and linkage levers are arranged at hand by the driver's right, with the handbrake and a toolbox to the left. The biggest problem with the cabs is corrosion. Many cabs have a rust crisis on the doors, wings and often under the cladding within the cab. The problem has been now recognised, with new doors and wings available at £350 and £65 +VAT respectively from Stewart Agricultural Ltd.

Nearing the end of production in 1990, County used an updated Hara cab which featured a new styling, a few modifications and refinements. The tractors which used this cab also received the Benson Group red colour scheme.

Driving

After climbing the steep and narrow steps, one has to manoeuvre around the tight lower door frame into position. Once seated, you begin to realise what an excellent all around view the cab gives. The very low side windows help to give you an impressive, elevated driving position.

After a few engine turnovers, the engine bursts into life with plenty of smoke to show for it. A moderate force is required to use the clutch pedal and the hefty gear levers move freely into gear.

Once moving the tractors lack of steering soon becomes apparent. If a tight turn is required, the independent brakes could be

the quickest way. Brakes are positive and bring you to halt with a little effort.

The view to the front is somewhat obstructed by the large exhaust, raised air cleaner and long nose. Though the side and rear views are a lot better, making hitching implements easy.

Overall the 1184 gives a very good driving environment, if accessed only a few times in a day. ➡

The flat floor Hara cab was a pleasant working environment, but was prone to rot and rust.

The majority of the controls, inluding the radio, were moved to the dashboard in the cab.

Useful contacts

Robb Morgan
County Parts
Craven Arms, Shropshire
01588 672390

A.T. Osborne
County Parts
Romsey, Hants
023 80814340

Adrian Tavernor
County Parts
Ludlow, Shropshire
01584 890276

Jas P Wilson
County forestry conversions and parts
Dumfries
01556 612233

Stewart Agricultural Ltd.
New Hara cab doors and wings
Inverurie, Aberdeenshire
01467 681418

Verdict

Despite the manoeuvrability issues that nearly all equal wheel County's have, the 1184 continues to excel in many operations. Its supreme stability and traction ensure that it can go everywhere and do almost anything.

With rusting cabs being the biggest killer of these tractors, high houred machines still continue to give sterling service.

Although many County models are becoming hard to find, many of the low houred or mint machines are now demanding higher premiums. These mint 1184 tractors can fetch anything from £15,000 upwards.

The majority of tractors will fall into the £7000-12000 bracket. While rough examples possibly for spares could still see around £5000.

Whatever condition, an 1184 would make a good investment, as it was one of the only few models which was made right till the end of the Company.

Acknowledgements
Paul Brown from Gatwick, Sussex for the use of photos and to Adrian Tavernor for the use of his tractor and information supplied. ■

Parts availability and how much?

Model	Year from	Year to	Mechanical	Bodywork	C	1	2	3
1394	1979	1990	5	2	£15,000	£12,000	£7,000	£4,000

(Guide - C: Concours condition, 1: Excellent condition with no faults, 2: Tidy condition and useable, 3: Rough condition, for restoration or possibly breaking. Parts availability scored out of 5).

This later 1184 belonged to Paul Brown from Gatwick and was sold at Cheffins Vintage Sale in October 2009 for £19,600.

County 1184 TW

Scots County family

Kim Jackson went to meet the McWhirter family in late October at their home in a stunning and wild part of Ayrshire, Scotland. Their nearest village is the beautiful village of Straiton and at the end of a nearby narrow road, you unexpectedly find two Countys – an 1184TW and a 1174.

Neil's grandfather arrived at Straiton in 1900 at the age of 3, and grew up with Clydesdale horses. The first tractor was a second hand Fordson Standard N on steels that arrived during World War 2.

Mr McWhirter senior was extremely mechanically minded and it was not long before the stables were devoid of anything equine. His excellent choice of first tractor was followed by a Ferguson TE-20 and David Brown 25D, the first new tractor on the farm. Massey Ferguson 35s also found their way to Straiton and the first four-wheel drive was a Roadless 65, not a commonplace tractor for a hill farm in Ayrshire.

At this time a drainage contractor friend of Neil's father Ian, was running County's which were sometimes required to work on the farm. Ian admired them greatly and took the very bold step of ordering an 118hp 1174 from Lloyds a Ford franchise. (Their head office is still in Carlisle but today they operate as New Holland dealers).

This was at a time when a 70hp tractor was considered more than adequate on many stock farms and even ten years ago the average horsepower for a new tractor on a United Kingdom farm was less than 100. The imposing sight of the tractor on local roads soon became a talking point.

The 1174 came with a Ford digger on the back; the backhoe was transplanted by Lloyds from a previous Ford industrial to fit the County. The McWhirters realised this was a mistake, because the extremely powerful and expensive piece of kit, ended up being idle 90 per cent of the time. Therefore a separate digger was purchased and the backhoe removed from the 1174. This then became the main tractor on the farm, working alongside two-wheel drive John Deeres.

At that time, most of the field work was carried out by the McWhirters or their staff. When Neil's brother John left school in 1985 to work on the farm full-time, he managed to supplement his income by doing some contract ploughing with the 1174. ➡

The 1184TW has been well maintained over the years, and cosmetically restored as the mechanical elements were in first rate order, but there never was the intention to do it to concours standard.

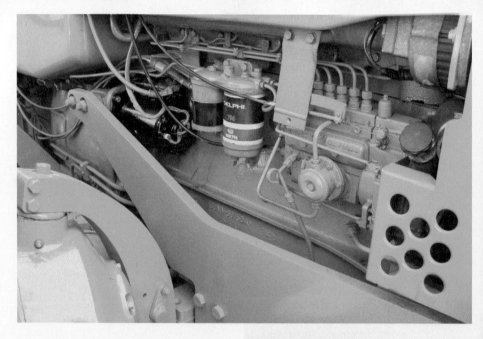

The 1174 is still an operational tractor and has completed 4,300 hours but is in sound condition. One of the reasons for this is that in common with the rest of the fleet it is stored undercover.

The original wheels were in good order but the tyres were worn and in need of replacement. The McWhirters found a set of wheels and tyres originally fitted to a drilling rig at a very reasonable price. So these were fitted as a unit to the County. Unfortunately the replacement wheels do not match the livery of the originals but the cost saving over a new set of tyres made this more than acceptable.

New doors have also been fitted as after all it is 30 years old and resides on a livestock farm; a new back window frame has been purchased, and is waiting to be fitted.

A SAME was acquired in 1990 and this became the main tractor for a while, but County was still held in very high regard by the McWhirters. In 2000 Ian McWhirter attended an arable farm sale at Balerno, on the outskirts of Edinburgh where the farmer was retiring.

There were four Countys listed and when he had looked over them, Ian rang his son John and they decided that the 1184 would be a welcome addition at Straiton. Ian made the successful bid and acquired the County for the farm.

The 1184TW now did every job that was thrown at it and it was decided early on that it would benefit from having a turbocharger retro-fitted. The now defunct TB Turbos from Lancaster travelled north to undertake the work, a fairly common procedure. TB Turbos even had a suitable turbo kit for an 1164TW export model sitting on the shelf. Once installed, it was tested on TB Turbos' dynamometer and this recorded an output of 128hp at the shaft; in comparison with the original engine output of 120hp and about 100hp at the shaft.

The paint finish looks good, with the bonnet sides reflecting the tyres.

The farm holding, in common with many in the last few years, has been restructured by the McWhirters'. The result of this is John and Ian are almost full time stockmen, the only workers on the farm, leaving the field work to be carried out by contractors. The income from the farm is derived from beef and lamb; they have 120 suckler cows and 800 Scottish Black-Face ewes.

This left the 1184TW to carry out general farm work inclusive of muck and slurry spreading. Rather unusually the McWhirters have always spread their own lime. The hourmeter on the 1184TW had climbed to 5,000 hours by now of which the McWhirters were responsible for about 1,000 of them.

About three years ago it was decided the 1184TW deserved its retirement with an awareness that the prices of classic tractors had risen, especially County's, and the 1184TW would be an asset worth protecting for the future.

Neil McWhirter, although still greatly interested in the farm has had a life-long interest in trucks, an interest he shares with his father Ian. When he left school he began an apprenticeship, and is now an HGV mechanic, working for P & C Hamilton of Girvan, who specialise in refrigerated haulage.

Many of his skills learned on the trucks, are transferable to tractors, and to put it simply he is an extremely useful family asset. Hence over the years Neil has found himself in charge of the workshop at Straiton and it was he who oversaw the 1184TW restoration.

Over the course of the few years the McWhirters, ran the 1184TW it had always been regularly serviced, and all of the mechanical faults fixed. The spares had come from County Tractors in Hampshire, who still have most parts for the tractor in stock.

One part which was needed and had been discontinued was the pump for the windscreen wipers, but once John had dismantled the old one, he managed to correct the fault. Before any cosmetic work to the tractor was undertaken it was felt

prudent to change all the oil-seals and a new hydraulic pump was refitted.

Not surprisingly the paintwork of the 1184TW was showing signs of age. To restore the paintwork the McWhirters sent

it to Colin Stewart and he blast cleaned the cab and repainted it. As is the case on most live-stock farms it is the cab that suffers the most, from constant usage and being in such a hostile environment. Colin Stewart also attended to the restoration of the bonnet, but left the skid unit for Ian to repaint.

One of the last jobs to be carried out; was the application of new decals which had come from County Tractors, which put the finishing touches to the repaint.

The tractor also needed new tyres, but the McWhirters didn't want to go to the expense of buying new ones, for a tractor which would only be used for occasional light work. Two back tyres were found with a lime spreading contractor, and the front ones came from Redpath Tyres at Duns.

Sharp-eyed observers may also note that the wheels are non-original as they are off a combine and were converted by a friend of Ian's. The wheel centres were cut out then a spacer ring welded in to increase the wheel track by four inches per wheel. Then the hub taking the wheel nuts was welded back to the spacer.

The 1184TW is an imposing machine and side on there is no indication of its width

The 1184TWs were in production from 1979 and the first ones used the same engines as the Ford TW-10. When the TW-15 appeared, County used TW-15 specification engines for their 1184TW, choosing not to amend their model name.

that now stands at approximately 10 feet, which certainly grabs the attention and more than a second look.

So where to next? Well, there is a very good one owner 1174 perhaps in need of a tidy up and fresh paint! ■

John McWhirter steps out of the 1184TW cab, to his brother Neil and Neil's son Jack.

The home Countys

Jamie Leigh brought a County flagship, the 1884 model, back to England and impresses Howard Sherren.

As many enthusiasts are well aware, those blue equal-wheeled tractors built by County Commercial Cars, of Fleet, Hampshire, now have an incredible following with price tags to match.

The interest in County models has never been higher, with prices doubling, if not tripling, within just a decade; one of County's 'big-wheelers' is at the top of many people's wish-list.

At 188hp and weighing in at just over eight tons, this monster of a machine is still an impressive piece of kit by today's standards – as it was back in the early 1980s.

The largest 1474 and 1884 models still remain the most desirable due to their limited production numbers. So far, approximately two dozen of the larger 1884 models have been accounted for - with not many people knowing how many there are still to be found or taken into preservation.

The majority of machines now are in the hands of British collectors, with a couple of machines known to be in Belgium and New Zealand.

The tractor which is the subject of this feature is one of a pair of machines brought back into the UK.

The County 1884 (serial number 47294 and registration AEV 733X) started life at the well-known Wallasea Farms on Wallesea Island

in Essex. Registered on October 6, 1981, it was supplied as one of a pair of 1884s to cultivate re-claimed marshland, which was predominately growing wheat.

After working the same ground for five years, the tractors went their separate ways in July 1986 and this one was sold to Scantlebury Manwood Ltd at Harlow, Essex – another arable farm where it was the prime mover for ploughing and cultivation.

The final result could be described as perfect. It certainly turned heads at the Cheshire Show.

In 1990 the tractor headed to Holland where it again joined an 1884 and was fitted with a huge pipeline crane (it is thought an extra clock was fitted to the machines in Holland and they recorded 2,000 hours of pipe work in 14 years.)

The owners coated both machines in a bright orange and white paint scheme, which meant they could be seen for miles. The paint protected the tractors from rust and rot, but wasn't enough to stop them getting abused.

Each tractor had numerous parts missing, bent or broken by the time this part of their careers ended and they were put up for auction in Holland towards the end of 2003.

The word spread on the County scene and high prices were expected. In the end both machines were bought by UK customers after a fierce bidding session and they returned home to Britain.

Jamie Leigh had decided one of these machines had to be his on a visit to a Lincolnshire dealer's yard.

"I went to look at a different County but when I saw this 1884 I thought it had to be mine, " he said. So the deal was done on a Saturday morning to buy the tractor – without the gigantic pipe crane, which helped to save a few pennies.

The sister tractor from Holland was also snapped up by an enthusiast and also headed off to be restored to its original form.

Jamie had his brought back to his place of work which happened to be John Bownes Ltd, of Winsford, Cheshire, renowned for its link with Roadless tractors and Ford conversions.

Spending most of his time in the workshop, Jamie had access to the dynometer and set about checking out the engine of his purchase in January 2004. ➡

Useful contacts

Baldini Tyres
Winsford
Cheshire
01606 883279

John Bownes Ltd
Winsford
Cheshire
01606 592639
www.johnbownes.co.uk

Bowland Tractors
Winsford
Cheshire
01606 863414
www.bowland-tractors.co.uk

DWB Engineering
Little Budworth
Cheshire
01829 760416

David Edge Auto Electrical
Eaton
Cheshire
01829 732295

KC Autos Bodyshop
Winsford
Cheshire
01606 861648

Adrian Tavernor
Ludlow
Shropshire
01584 890276

Robert Wraight
Ashford
Kent
01233 622985
www.robertwraightltd.com

Jamie said: "I took a big gamble; with the cab in a very poor state and no controls I had to carry out the restoration to make the machine useable."

So with this in mind, Robert Wraight from Kent found a Ford TW-35 which could be used as a donor tractor. With just under 4,000 hours on the clock, this tractor had extremely straight panel work and a very tidy cab. It provided nearly everything Jamie needed to bring the 1884 back into action.

David Bland, of Bowland Tractors, who works from the same yard as the Bownes family, also helped to locate the difficult-to-find items.

Above: Bashed and beaten, this County 1884 was worked hard in Holland, from where it was imported back to England.

Results could not have been better: plenty of poke was on tap, but this was the only check he could carry out as the previous owners had gutted the side console and the pto control to operate the crane was all that was left.

With no spools or linkage, the tractor could not really be tested to its full potential.

Work began by stripping the tractor down, removing the cab and replacing broken or incorrect parts ready for a sand-blasting. As a bare, rolling chassis, the front tombstone could be replaced as it was cracked, the stops removed from the axle to reduce oscillation and linkage added along with a pick-up hitch to make it more useable.

The spool valves were now included while the intercooler was swapped and a new water pump fitted just to be on the safe side.

The bare skid found its way into the hands of Dave Bloor at DWB Engineering, just 10 minutes down the road from Jamie's home.

Here it received a thorough sand-blasting by Harvey Leech to obtain a good base for a perfect paint job. Back home the tractor had the front axle driveshaft seals replaced before being treated to numerous coats of filler primer and at least 10 litres of New Holland's Ford Tractor blue paint in the workshop.

The old cab was designated scrap, thanks to the amount of modifications that had been carried out, missing parts and the rot which had set in. The replacement TW cab was stripped out completely and the frame received multiple coats of paint before having the glass re-fitted.

A cab cladding kit from PJ Dring & Co replaced the aging roof liner and damaged fender foam. The inside of the cab was finished off with a new floor mat from Uphill Sales and Service from Wiltshire and a genuine Ford radio.

Outside the 'unique' County hinges were again fabricated by Harvey at DWB

Engineering, who made a cracking job of reproducing these hard-to-get-hold-of items. ➡

1884 specifications

Engine	Ford 401 DFT
Power (hp)	188
Max power @ (rpm)	2,200
Max pto power (hp)	156
Cylinders	6TI
Displacement (cc)	6,578
Bore (mm)	111.8
Stroke (mm)	111.8
Fuel capacity (litres)	465
Standard transmission	Dual Power 16 forward 4 reverse
Top speed (mph)	19.82
Turning radius (mm)	15,000
Length (mm)	5,300
Width (mm)	2,500
Weight (kg)	8,030
Tyre size	18.4 R38
Produced	1980-89
Cab	Q
Price new	£29, 850

The last new model to be built by County Commercial Cars was this 188hp turbocharged and intercooled monster, the 1884.

Dave next turned his attention to mirroring the left-hand steps for the articles missing on the right; again his workmanship couldn't be faulted. The final touch was locating the correct plough lights for the front of cab which, after much searching, surprisingly came from the unloading auger on a New Holland TX combine.

Next to complete were the wheels, which required a fair bit of preparation. New 18.4 R38 Goodyear STRs were required to complete the 'original' look. The first pair were found early-on and fitted by locally-based Baldini Tyres, who also swapped another new pair from an old family farm tractor when it was traded in.

With the tyres sorted, Jamie set about the laborious task of returning the rims to a perfect finish. He said: "They were extremely badly pitted, it took at least seven coats of paint to obtain the finish I wanted and get them to the current condition."

The hard work is apparent just by looking at the fantastic shine the rims give off. The shine continues on the 1884's sheet metal and bonnet, which were professionally painted by bodyshop specialists KC Autos in Winsford; decals were provided by County expert Adrian Tavernor.

Cab was completely stripped out and gained new cladding with a new floor mat.

Original Ford oil filters came courtesy of Geoff in the stores at John Bownes which, without a doubt, makes the machine that little bit more unique.

The end result surely is nothing but perfect; the attention to detail is shocking and Jamie now has a tractor that looks better than new and which will certainly turn heads.

Its first official outing was to the Cheshire Show, where it towed the Beeston YFC float and led the procession around the ring, showing off four years of hard work. ∎

Linkage and spools were missing from the tractor when Jamie bought it, but they are all back in place along with a Ford TW pick-up hitch.

King of traction

Equal-wheeled tractors have an incredible following with the price tags to match. You cannot get more popular than the biggest County of all, the 188hp County 1884. Howard Sherren investigates this particular model, explains why it is so special and points out important areas – if you ever get the chance or have the money to contemplate buying one.

The boom for County models has never been higher, with prices doubling, if not tripling within just a decade. One of County's 'big-wheelers' is at the top of many people's wish-list: at 188hp and weighing in at just over eight tons, this is certainly still an impressive machine by today's standards, as much as it was back in the early-'80s.

The largest 1474 and 1884 models still remain the most desirable due to their limited production numbers. So far approximately two dozen of the larger 1884 models have been accounted for, with not many people knowing how many there are still to be found or taken into preservation.

The majority of machines now are held in the hands of collectors both here and in Northern Ireland, with a couple of machines known to be overseas in Belgium and New Zealand, for example. Within the United Kingdom, two keen collectors can account for a quarter of the total produced, so they are safe for the near future in preservation. But what if you had the chance to buy one? ➡

Top of many enthusiasts' wish-lists – the 1884.

At 188hp and just over eight tons, the 1884 is a monster of a machine and an impressive sight working.

The original Ford TW-30, on which the 1884 was based, was launched on 4th March 1979 at the Sima show in Paris, and the new tractor gathered a great deal of interest amongst large farmers and contractors. It was not until the Smithfield Show in 1980 that County introduced its 1884 for £29,850, County's answer to farmers' demands for a high-horsepower machine capable of extremely heavy cultivation.

Nothing else could quite pull like it or quite resembled it. The main production centre for the TW range was Antwerp where models were produced for Britain, Europe and most of the export markets, but manufacture also took place in Romeo, mainly in two-wheel drive form for the North American market. The Antwerp factory eventually took over the full production from Romeo.

Prior to the 1884, the Muir Hill 171 was one of the biggest equal-wheel rigid-frame machines before moving onto articulated models. Also the International Harvester 3588 and 6588 2+2 were the only other machines to be launched at the beginning of production and have similar statistics.

With equal wheels, 180hp six-cylinder IH turbocharged engine and similar weight; the two machines were well matched to the big County. The later 180hp IH 5288 was also available in 1982, but again small front wheels let the machine down for traction. The Ford TW-30 may have had a similar specification, but tractive capabilities were somewhat reduced: even ballasted up the TW would struggle to perform as the 1884 did.

John Deere had its 4650 model which at 190hp was again in the same power bracket and available from 1983, before moving onto the articulated 215hp 8440 in a different class of machine.

Intercooling for greater output

During the 1970s Ford needed higher-horsepower engines to compete with other leading manufacturers, and so looked at ways of getting more power out of the 6.6 litre engine as fitted to the existing 8700 and 9700 models which were in production. They had already gone as far as possible with

turbo-charging engines, so the next logical step would be to charge air-cooling.

This design used an intercooler fitted in conjunction with the turbo to cool the air before it entered the cylinders. Cooler air has greater density and because of this, a larger volume of fuel can be burnt in the correct air-to-fuel ratio, and therefore give an increase in power.

The chosen design was an 'Air to Air' system, simply because it could be fitted to the current 6.6 litre engine with fewest alterations and it was also proven on Mack trucks. The design, consisting of a

The 6.6-litre Ford 401 engine was turbocharged and intercooled to obtain nearly 190hp in the Ford TW-30 and County 1884. At the time it was one of the first machines to feature air-to-air intercooling.

turbocharger with a tip turbine fan and an air cooler was developed in conjunction with the AiResearch division of the Garrett Corporation.

Big bore and short stroke

The 1884 used Ford's proven 'big bore-short stroke' 6.6 litre engine equipped with a turbocharger and under piston cooling. The TW-30 engine, intercooled to give greater output, was not only a first for Ford tractor operations, but was also the first agricultural tractor to feature the 'air to air' design. It also had an oil cooler mounted on the side of the engine.

This, as well as two vertically-mounted oil filters, reduced oil temperatures by 20 per cent and service intervals were increased to 300 hours. In-line Lucas CAV Minimec fuel pumps were used on all of Ford's 401 cu in. engines: they were very reliable in service and cold morning start-up was excellent with the aid of an excess fuel button.

With the introduction of the TW Series, a new larger engine oil pump was re-located, and driven off the front of the crankshaft. The fact was that the pump was too big for the engine and meant that the excess oil had to be dumped past the relief valve. This resulted in some unusual side loading of the relief valve, which caused it to leave a ridge in the bore, which if it became big enough, could cause the valve to stick in the open position.

This can cause oil pressures of well over 100 PSI on start up and a sudden drop at lower speeds. The engine can become porous as with some Fords, so check the oil for milky residues. The diesel capacity was significantly more thanks to a belly tank which increased the 1884's capacity by 111 litres over the TW-30 to 465.

Assistor rams and Dowdeswell Engineering lift rods are worth looking out for as they are difficult to obtain today.

Dual Power

The transmission used was a 16x4 Dual Power unit, known as the "crash box". It was awkward to use during both field and road use, though it rarely gave any problems and time proved that it was very reliable.

The Dual Power system incorporated a rugged planetary gear set located directly behind the clutch in the bell housing and an electrically-controlled hydraulic clutch which was operated via a foot switch located on the cab floor. Once depressed, the groundspeed was reduced by 22 per cent and torque increased by 28 per cent, it also doubled all available gear ratios.

The principle of the design was similar to that of rival Multi-Power, Torque Amplifier, and Power Synchron systems, yet Ford's Dual Power gave outstanding reliability, and remained virtually unchanged throughout its existence.

A powerful Webster pump was used as the main hydraulic pump on the County, a second pump was a low-pressure unit which operated the Dual Power clutches, differential lock, independent PTO clutch and lubricated the driveline components. The power brakes on the 1884 were also operated by this second pump. Hydraulic trailer brakes and a third spool valve were factory-fitted extras.

New force of skid units

In 1983, a new phase of TWs was introduced, again at the Sima show in Paris and they received re-powered engines and other improvements. The TW30's fuel system was also tweaked to boost output to 195bhp: 11 per cent more power was claimed by Ford for the new TW series engines and was amongst the lowest-rated engine speeds for this horsepower in agriculture.

A new temperature-sensing variable speed viscous cooling fan was fitted to all engines. That worked at full speed only "…when the engine coolant exceeds normal operating temperature." Increased horsepower and better fuel efficiency were the result. This was also helped by the flow-matched and precisely-manufactured Lucas CAV Minimec fuel pump. Almost no engine power was used for the cooling which gave more power at the drawbar.

The 1884 had a single 1,000 rpm PTO and multiple disc brakes which were also self-equalising. Lift capacity was excellent at ➡

6,670kg when the twin assistor rams were fitted. Unique linkage lift rods designed in conjunction with Dowdeswell should be looked at, as if not present or broken, replacements will not be available.

County axles

The 1884 used a similar axle to that on the earlier 1454, same hubs but with a wider track. Parts for these are quite easy to obtain through specialists such as A T Osbourne and Adrian Tavernor. Bearings may eventually fail here and can be around £70 or more to replace, play can often be down to incorrect shimming so it is best to investigate this first.

Seals are a very common problem and leaks can often be seen, but again seals are relatively cheap to replace. The unique twin drive shafts will need careful checks for wear in the universal joints and splines, replacement parts should still be available too.

Up front, the unique 'big' County light housing can be sometimes bent and beaten,

Lift capacity with twin assistor rams was over six tons, adequate for most machinery then and now.

The competition: 1982

Make/Model	County 1884	Ford TW-30/35	IH 3588/6588	JD 4650	Muir-Hill 171	MB-Trac 1500
Engine	Ford 401 DFT	Ford 401 DFT	IH 466B	JD 6466A	Perkins V8.540	Mercedes
Engine power (bhp)	188	188	180	190	177	150
Max power @	2200	2200	2400	2200	2500	2400
Number of cylinders	6TI	6TI	6T	6TI	8	6T
Displacement (cc)	6578	6578	7636	7640	8834	5675
Bore (mm)	111.8	111.8	109.2	115.8	108	97
Stroke (mm)	111.8	111.8	135.9	120.6	120.7	128
Fuel capacity (litre)	465	354	579	386	318	170
Top speed (mph)	19.82	19.00	20.00	18.00	17.99	24.00
Standard transmission	Dual Power 16 Forward x 4 Reverse	Dual Power 16 Forward x 4 Reverse	Torque Amp. 16 Forward x 8 Reverse	Powershift 15 Forward x 4 Reverse	Synchro 10 Forward x 2 Reverse	Synchro 14 Forward x 14 Reverse
Turning circle (mm)	15000	12800	9720	10800	11420	13000
Length (mm)	5300	4750	5800	5420	4730	4680
Min. width (mm)	2500	2124	1600	2743	2450	2480
Standard weight (kg)	8030	6600	7493	8224	6350	6220
Std. tyre size front	18.4 R38	18.4 R38	18.4 R38	16.9 R30	18.4 R34	18.4 R34
Std. tyre size back	18.4 R38	18.4 R38	18.4 R38	20.8 R42	18.4 R34	18.4 R34
Cab	Q	Q	IH	SG2	Muir Hill	MB
Produced from	1980	1979	1979	1983		1980
Produced to	1989	1982	1984	1988		1987
Price new	£37,121	£36,322	N/A	£41,409	N/A	£32,740

The flagship model from County is now highly sought after and commands very high prices.

Left: Door hinges were unique to County which enabled the door to clear the 18.4 R38 tyres.

so may require fabrication here. 16 weights are hung upon the front and are definitely worth finding, as prices can be up to £1,500 or more for a set of genuine examples, though new copies are available from Mark at A T Osbourne.

Ford's Q cab
All current and previous TW models used the Ford Q cab, which included the mighty 1884. The cab was designed and built by GKN Sankey and gave a low noise level of 83 dBA. The interior was made to last and wore well, but replacement parts such as roof linings, cab cladding and floor mats are all available as after-market parts.

Points worth noting here are the special door hinges which allowed the doors to swing past the enormous front wheels, as if not present they are awkward to obtain or manufacture. The cab steps were also unique, fitting snugly between the wheels.

They can often be found bent or missing, but luckily are fairly easy to reproduce in the right hands.

Cab-mounted plough lights are often missing and obtaining the right ones can be a tricky job, but owners say that New Holland TX unloading auger work lights are identical and most likely the best replacement. Two machines were fitted with Super Q roof moldings, both are now in the hands of one well-known collector.

There is nothing more impressive than a County 1474 or 1884 in terms of physical presence, thanks to the huge equal 38" wheels, long bonnet and 2.5m width.

Although they share the majority of parts with the Ford TW, the tractor is still special and has a price tag to match. Recent tractors have exchanged for thousands and the price tag is rapidly approaching six figures, so you'd better start saving if you want one!

Acknowledgements
Thanks to Jamie Leigh from Cheshire for the use of his tractor. ∎

Last of the Countys

It was a very sad time for both employees and customers when County Commercial Cars called in the receivers in 1983. However, all was not yet lost as the company carried on under the ownership of David Gittins and later the Benson Group. We look at some of the last tractors to carry the County name.

In 1987 County Tractors was taken over by the Benson Group, a concern better known for owning Bamfords and Teleshift. The company was also the importer of Valmet tractors that fought for space alongside Countys as favourites to work in British woods. When the acquisition was made, the company moved production from the original site in Fleet, Hampshire, to its home at Knighton in Powys.

With around 40,000 tractors produced worldwide, it is believed that only some further 150 tractors were produced before production ceased in early 1990. The models that remained in production included the 774, 974 and 1184 examples, in addition to three long-nose 1474 models and two 1884 flagship tractors.

The problems sourcing cabs for UK legislation became the biggest killer for Benson and only a handful of tractors were fitted with the new cab and finished in the striking red Benson livery.

The very last tractors out of Knighton included four 1184 models which used a Ford 10 series box, a synchronised Dual Power unit fitted in addition to this newly-developed cab.

It featured full-length glass doors in addition to glass-reinforced plastic (GRP) dashboard and side console to bring it up to date.

Although the specifications of the tractors remained relatively unchanged, the limited numbers of these last machines made them rather special.

Rescued from the Falklands, this 1184 was one of the last tractors built by the Benson Group. All photos: Howard Sherren.

Restored to a high standard, the tractor made a staggering £47,000 at a Cheffins vintage sale in 2010.

Of the four that were produced, two were supplied to UK contractors and they are still working for a living. Another went to Siberia and the last to the Falklands.

This last tractor returned to the UK in late 2009, where a dealer was lucky enough to buy it back from the Falklands government. This particular 1184, built on the 11th December 1990 and with serial 50010 started-off in red but was soon wearing the statutory yellow, industrial paint. It was subjected to a thorough restoration and returned to its former 'Benson Red' glory. It was sold at the Cheffins' Spring Vintage Sale to a Cheshire collector.

One more chance

Although Benson continued in business without County tractors, one more batch of Countys were produced in the mid 1990s. SEM Engineering Ltd of Basildon, Essex, acquired rights from the Benson Group to use the County name to produce a number of tractors for export.

The first tractor produced was HSH140, which was based on Ford's six-cylinder 8340 skid unit. The 140hp Powerstar engine propelled the two-wheel-drive tractor to a colossal 30mph and was ideal for transport operations. This tractor was ideally suited to the farming operations of South Africa.

County axles were also modified for other 40 Series skid units such as the 85hp 764-40 which used the four-cylinder 6640 engine, the 135hp 1164-40 was also based on 8340

but featured no cab and finally the 1184-40, which received a cab.

Sadly, SEM Engineering went into receivership in 1995, so the production of ➡

Another tractor to be rescued from the Falklands. This 1184-40 is believed to be the only one in left.

Below: In good original order, the low 2,150 hours figure was believed to be genuine.

this batch of tractors was moved back to Knighton and finished during April 1995.

The full batch of 10 tractors were finally completed in July 1995, all were based on the 40 Series Fords and were destined for the Falklands, St Helena and Canada.

A total of two 1184-40 models were produced and sent to the Falklands with one returning to the UK in January 2009 after the other was destroyed in a fire.

The 1184-40 carried a serial number 70022 and registration F1526 and was rescued by a collector from the south-west of the country. It too came up at the Cheffins vintage sale but didn't meet its reserve.

County's unique drive system meant it was difficult to convert any later and more advanced skid units.

For further reading on the history of County Tractors, please see the books *Ford Tractor Conversions* or *County Pictorial Review* by Stuart Gibbard. ∎

Roots in Doncaster

Good examples of IH's 634 model are hard to find and four-wheel drive derivatives are even more desirable. Howard Sherren tracks down one of County's other derrivatives, the International Harvester 634 All-Wheel Drive.

International Harvester's 634 was not the most popular choice for farmers in the late 1960s because its dated and crude design was off-putting.

Those who could see beyond that, though, found it perfect for their requirements because its performance was far superior to that of the opposition.

Heavily over-engineered, the 634 was built for heavy draft work and could easily out-perform the equivalent Ford 5000, for example. International's long-stroke, four-cylinder BD-281 engine produced an impressive 66hp at just 1,600rpm and this low-down grunt meant the tractor would just keep on going, even in the most difficult of situations.

Weighing just under three tonnes, traction was never really an issue. However, as

implements got bigger and wider, traction soon did become a problem for any tractor and getting that crucial power to the ground was a priority.

Four-wheel drive was becoming steadily more popular at the time and there was a number of manufacturers that had recognised the gap in the market and begun to offer large four-wheel drive machines to handle the extra workload created by the push for greater farm productivity. ➡

Front axle kits were fitted to International Harvester skid units by County, which adapted the design from its successful Ford versions.

The turning circle was something of a disappointment at 13m but could be halved when using the independent brakes.

The most famous four-wheel drive manufacturers were County Commercial Cars and Roadless Traction Ltd, who both took commonplace Ford skid units and converted them into four-wheel drive for added traction and safety.

With two equal wheels on the County kit the stability of the two-wheel drive skid was vastly improved and traction obviously doubled.

It was during the Sixties that both firms extended their horizons beyond Ford skids and started to experiment with other manufacturers, converting their axles to fit on a number of different machines in kit form.

Roadless prototyped its unequal wheel design on another British-built machine, the International Harvester B-450 and around 25 were built by IH between 1963 and 1970. Roadless continued to supply kits for the larger B-614 and around 50 more were converted over the years.

At the same time County prototyped its equal-wheel axle on the B-614, which later

634 AWD specifications

Engine	IH BD-281
Power (hp)	66
Rated speed (rpm)	1,600
Cylinders	4
Torque (lb/ft)	225
Max torque @ (rpm)	1,200
Fuel capacity (litres)	77.28
Transmission	8 forward 4 reverse
Top speed (mph)	15.9
Turning radius (mm)	11,000
Length (mm)	3,810
Width (mm)	1,530
Turning circle (mm)	12,800
Weight (kg)	4,343
Tyre size (front)	12x38
Tyre size (rear)	12x38

With four equal wheels and added weight, the pulling power of the 634 AWD was incredible.

went into production on the replacement in 1969. This 634 model with its equal wheels was dubbed the 'All Wheel Drive.'

Interestingly, International Harvester continued ordering kits from Roadless for the 634 so this particular model came in three guises between 1969 and 1972 - two-wheel, four-wheel and all-wheel drive versions: plenty of choice!

The County axle took its drive through different rear half-shafts which took power down a shaft either side of the machine to the County hubs and front axle which were bolted to side plates, increasing the strength of the machine.

The rest of the tractor remained relatively unchanged, although new foot plates were fitted to allow the shafts to pass safely underneath, power steering was standard and a new front weight block added even more weight. The weight was now up to 4,343kg and with its four equal 12x38 or 14x34 wheels the traction was immense.

The eight-forward and two-reverse transmission gave a disappointing top speed of just 16mph on the tallest wheels, unlike other County machines which were renowned for their rocketing top speed on the road, but at the time this wasn't a major issue. The tractors were built for field work, not transport operations.

As with any 634, engine starting was an issue for many machines or for operators who weren't educated on how to start them properly. If heater plugs didn't function it would be nearly impossible to start the machines and if the battery wasn't up

The All-Wheel Drive models had a special decal in addition to this one, but it's missing from this 634.

to scratch it would also lead to further problems.

The turning circle was additionally quite shocking at just under 13m, but luckily less than halved to 5.6m when the brakes were anchored on in conjunction.

In 'All Wheel Drive' form, it is believed 50 or so tractors were built and sold, considerably less than the 200 Roadless four-wheel drive versions.

The durability made them both ideal for work in forestry and a number of models were sold into the woods for logging duties. This is where a number sadly spent their life and where they would rust away and end up

being scrapped.

Thankfully, the majority were saved by enthusiasts and collectors who have either restored them or managed to get the machines back into work after years of neglect.

They still make an interesting sight between the sea of blue equal-wheel Countys and Doe tractors and yellow Muir-Hill models. Their rarity has also pushed the price up considerably with the last tractor selling at auction in immaculate original order for a staggering £17,200.

Thanks to Stephen and Matthew Haylock for use of their tractor. ∎

Stability and safety were increased on the AWD so many went into forestry operations, where they were sadly abused.

The Leyland 4100 had an imposing stance.

Spreading the word

Bob Weir finds one of County's rarer works in Scotland.

Mechanic Graham Hill has had a passion for the orange and blue for as long as he can remember. His list of credits includes a Nuffield Universal Three, 3/42, 10/60 and 4/65 as well as Leyland models 154, 344, 384, 270, 272, 282 and the occasional Marshall.

He said: "I first started getting interested in Nuffield and Leyland tractors when I was serving my time as a trainee. I liked the fact that they were relatively cheap to run and that they were all made at Bathgate in Scotland."

Graham, from Forfar in Tayside, can recall

that his first experience with the marque was when one of his friends decided to buy a model 4/60.

"When we got home we discovered that the tractor needed a new water pump," he recalls. "We went to visit a contact in Fife, who used to break half-a-dozen tractors every week. I remember thinking that compared to some of the other manufacturers, the parts seemed to be good value for money. I subsequently acquired a 4/65 and have never looked back."

That was in 1988. Graham has owned many standard specification tractors in the intervening years, and now specialises in conversions. He is a big believer in making

do with second-hand parts, and has now restored several machines.

His rare 1972 Leyland model 4100 is a recent acquisition, which he bought in 2009 from a dispersal sale, and which had been fully restored to almost its original condition.

Graham said: "The complete history of the machine is a bit of a grey area, but I have managed to trace it back to a dealer at Bishop Auckland in County Durham. I believe it was then involved in forestry work for several years before being snapped up by an enthusiast in Wales. The restoration is thought to have been carried out on his behalf by specialists Wyard-Scott, based in Bury St Edmunds."

He also believes it was during this period that the Leyland's cab went AWOL. According to Graham, the unit for the 4100 would have been originally made for Leyland by Victor, which subsequently became part of Airflow Streamline.

He thinks that his may have been damaged at some point, which was probably the reason it was removed. He is currently on the look-out for a suitable replacement – at the right price.

The equal-wheel four-wheel drive 4100 was one of a new range of tractors introduced by Leyland in 1972. Among other innovations, it was equipped with the company's new six-cylinder engine. The diesel had a bore/stroke of 3.858 x 4.921 inches (98 x 125mm) and was fitted with a cyclonic dry-type air cleaner. In 6/98 NT format it had a compression of 16.8:1 and was capable of delivering 100hp.

It was designed to eliminate the problems associated with its predecessor, a 100mm bore ex-BMC unit. The improvements included a new shell cast cylinder head using re-designed valves, porting and injector locations. Particular attention was paid to the liners and liner sealing.

The result was a long stroke engine offering the benefits of high torque at a low rpm, all for a modest fuel consumption. During the mid-Seventies the unit would go on to cement its reputation as one of the best tractor engines on the market.

There were also improvements to the transmission and hydraulics. The tractor was equipped with ten forward and two reverse gears using a sliding spur gear and epicyclic final drive. This was the same system as used on its stable mate, the 2100. The fully live hydraulics offered 2,600psi and 6,000lb of lift with the help of two assistor rams. Category 2 linkage was included, along with a live engine-mounted 9.2 gall/min gear pump. Other features included an automatic pick-up hitch.

In common with some of the company's competitors the designers at Leyland also put a lot of thought into the effects of noise and pollution, as well as the driver's creature comforts. The rubber-mounted engine and flat floor safety cab were so advanced that they incorporated many features that would eventually become legal requirements.

The model 4100 pre-dated Ford's decision to build 4WD tractors in-house and the machine's twin drive shafts were connected to a County front axle.

Graham said: "I am led to believe that when Leyland upgraded their engines from the four-cylinder to the six-cylinder, the standard brakes weren't really up to the task. The company decided to enlist the help of County, who were also responsible for supplying the four-wheel drive. Despite the tractor's ability very few models were actually built, and surviving examples are now quite rare." ■

The six-cylinder engine had plenty of grunt.

The dash panel.

The three-point linkage complete with pick-up hitch.

Monster from the deep

Peter Love tells the story of the unique NIAE County FC tyre test rig that was offered for sale in 2009. He was given the opportunity of a test drive around Dean Hill Park, Wiltshire, however on the sale day it wasn't sold.

If you want something different and are a keen collector of County equipment then the ultimate just has to be the former National Institute of Agricultural Engineers (NIAE) late 1969 County FC tyre testing rig. It was offered for sale by Cheffins on Saturday 9 May 2009 at Dean Hill Park near Salisbury, Wiltshire, but it never sold and has vanished into the deep again.

It was a sad day in 2007 when the final chapter unfolded on the Silsoe Research Institute at Wrest Park, Bedfordshire, and the former home of the de Gray family. The NIAE (National Institute of Agricultural

Engineering) had been in Bedfordshire since the late 1940's and previous to that in Oxfordshire.

It started in 1924 when it was called Institute of Agricultural Engineering and until the just post war period it had an experimental farm at Askham Bryan in Yorkshire as well. This is well documented on a couple of Old Pond Publishing Silsoe connected DVD's.

Without doubt the NIAE lead the way in the UK when it came to agricultural research technology, particularly in mechanisation and beyond. With a wider brief in the 90's the name changed to Silsoe Research

Institute, however now in the 21st century, funding and various other factors brought the facility to a sad close.

Naturally you needed to have apparatus to test the capabilities of what the manufacturers claimed and various testing rigs were to be used over the years for the calculations that were needed for the results. Here the famous but small drawbar dynamometer car used at Silsoe for many years in the 1950's is fondly remembered. That also applies to the Farmall M which drove the dynamo for the wheel/tyre tester that was driven from the electrical supply provided by the Farmall.

The ex-Silsoe test rig is an excellent running proposition with just over 3,000 hours on the clock.

SNM 498J

New test rig

A spacious new test rig was created in 1969 based on what I believe to be a County FC 1004 with the 2703E six-cylinder engine. However for some reason the press suggested a few years ago that the Silsoe tyre test rig was a FC 1164, which isn't correct from my understanding of things.

In fact the revolutionary forward control County design that came from the hand of David Tapp and Joe Davey had come along in 1965 as the FC654 with the four-cylinder Ford 5000 65bhp engine, and the rig was originally painted blue

What I do know is that the County test rig was revamped during its life with computer technology and a rear cab provided by Operator Control Cabs Ltd, Four Ashes, Wolverhampton. This all survives today, in immaculate condition and has been made to work again, including the computer.

Two transmissions

The interesting thing is the FC rig carries no less than two hydrostatic Lucas T100 transmission systems. One is for driving the tractor and the other is to power the tracked or wheel/tyre combinations that ran in a cradle behind the unit. Originally it was painted a very handsome County blue livery, but later on it ended up in the brown and beige livery it carries today.

It was in 1990 that the County FC test rig was quietly tucked away in the shed after completing much work on conventional and plastic tyres over the years. When offered for sale at the 2007 April Cheffins Vintage Collective, where a number of Silsoe tractors were sold, it wasn't in running condition.

However I'm pleased to say that when I had a drive of it in 2009 that was no longer the case. This was following the correction of a number of faults with the fuel system and various other components and the County ran and worked a treat. Richard Parry's staff did a wonderful job of fettling the machine up and it is a credit to all those involved in bringing this unique vehicle back to working condition again.

It was a great pleasure to be invited by Richard to see and drive the County test rig in action and take a look at the superb site, which is today called Dean Hill Park, and is situated near Salisbury. It was formally the Royal Naval Armament Depot, Dean Hill. Here armaments were mostly supplied to the naval base at Gosport and the surrounding area.

Richard has built up a considerable collection of veteran and vintage machinery assisted by the skills of 85 year old George Cobley and others, but had decided it was time to down size the collection, hence the sale that took place on Saturday 9 May.

Bill King and the team were brought in to sell his collection off, that went very well indeed but the mighty "Monster from the Deep" didn't make it at the sale and has disappeared again, but I will never forget having the chance to drive such a machine that's for sure, the hydrostatic transmission was very positive. ∎

This is what the County looked like in the early years.

The Lucas T-100 transmission system.

Inside the cab it's like new again and fully functional, thanks to Richard Perry's team.

The computer screen can all be demonstrated and used if required again.

A life in sales

Mike Gormley tells of life as a County salesman.

In my earlier days at County Commercial Cars Ltd, the team was Tim Kirtland (Wales and west of England and later southern Africa and Australasia), Guy Seaman took over from Tim in the west of England and later became assistant sales manager based at Fleet, Bruce Keech (Eastern Counties) Jock Hairs who looked after both sales and service for Scotland and the north and myself in the south. For a time there was also 'Mac' MacDonald who was resident in the USA and looked after North America - just a small patch!

We looked after field sales. Aftersales was covered by Johnny Heathers (south), Ken Ree (west of England), Gordon Williamson (northern England) and Stan Anderson (Eastern Counties). Before I joined there was Robin Disney who looked after central England for a short while. One of the few to move on.

John Hull supported all of us for demonstrations and other things! At Fleet Don Mole, as field operations manager, looked after day-to-day events and Peter Jaggard did the more serious business as sales manager. Heading up the sales team was Brian Taylor as sales director.

The service team was backed up by Frank Charlton who was service manger, supported by Dennis Smith and headed up by Geoff Tapp as their director. Spare parts were managed by Don (Taffy) Carter. We all had dealings with David Tapp, who was an engineer but also very focused on the end user and applications, and was engineering liaison director. David was the driver of the County Sea Horse that drove its way into the Guinness Book of Records as the first, and maybe the only tractor to drive/float itself across the English Channel.

Roger Thomas for a good many years looked after the PR side of life at Fleet. Roger and I had first met working on the same farm before both going to the Royal Agricultural College. We followed different paths and then came together again.

Tirn Kirkland eventually decided he had had enough of living overseas and, after many years, relinquished the post of manger for southern Africa. I am pleased to say I was asked to take Ns over which also included die Antipodes and Indian Ocean islands. Well, someone had to. It was the only overseas-based job in the company.

Nigel Taylor, Brian Taylor's son, had joined us and took over my UK territory. We had spent some time together in the UK and on overseas demo tours. Two other Tapp family members to spend time with the company were Jonathan Tapp and David Taylor, mostly working with John Hull on the demonstration side of the operation.

On the subject of overseas travel, there was plenty to go around. Most of us had an overseas territory as well as our home patch.

Ken looking over an 1164 in Crete. These were mostly used with huge single-furrow ploughs, as seen here, and often had dozer blades fitted to clear, level and plough olive groves. These were mostly very small areas in difficult and gard terrain. It was not uncommon for tractors to be broken in half on the huge embedded rocks.

For some of us it meant being away from home a great deal. If one of us was away for a while we often did a caretaker job on the vacant patch, which led to great variety.

I had not been with County all that long before I was off to Finland with David Tapp. We went into the arctic winter to see Countys working in the forests, a substantial market. I had my 'County wings' and was to soon get the travel bug that was ➡

Brian Brimacombe was often the driver of County's Ford Transcontinental demo truck when John Hull was unavailable. It is seen here in the station yard loaded and ready to go.

embedded in me for life. With County we travelled well, which made up in part for long periods away and long and anti-social hours. Over the years I clocked up about 50 countries; others must have had more in their passports.

Above, behind and on both sides of me was a team of many who kept the wheels of our industry turning. They gave us the product range and sorted out the problems and of course built the tractors and other products.

For a small company we had an extensive model range and an almost infinite range of options and specials. The range did not stop at tractors and included trucks and vans and other highly innovative products - especially in the earlier days.

Although I concentrate here on the people that actually worked for County I must mention the vast number of people for whom County was part of their lives as well. In the UK and worldwide there was a huge network of dealers and distributors, many of whom came to be very close to County.

Ford Motor Company was not only the principal supplier of components but in many countries was also the distributor of County products. In some cases such as South Africa, Countys were assembled the Ford line.

Also part of the scene were many of those involved in making and supplying equipment that was used in conjunction with Countys. A number of very close working relationships existed with companies who sometimes produced special equipment for County or items based on County products.

All in all it built into a massive worldwide network of people for whom County was very much part of their lives.

innovative and forward thinking people among them: Ernest and Percy Tapp, who founded the company, and Joe Davey, who was largely responsible for the County tractor design.

The relatively small team of people developed and evolved new ideas, many of which are still in evidence to this day. These include not only the County tractor in its many forms but also such concepts as waste disposal trucks that compact the rubbish (a County innovation), meat handling devices for lorries, additional axles on lorries to carry more load and a high-speed tractor (Trac Truck).

The 1939-45 war was a time of great innovation in the UK and County was course there. A light tank, the Praying Mantis, now at Bovington tank museum, a gunnery simulator, I believe the first ever, and many special winch trucks to handle the mass of barrage balloons were among the County war effort and their development was all down to the few highly inventive people. Tracked tractors moved to skid-steered wheeled tractors and thence to the County 4x4 systems, as we generally know them.

Following the demise of County Cars Ltd in 1983, many of the team was disbanded and of course by that time quite a number of the originals had retired or passed on.

County Tractors Ltd rose from the rubble (much of it now shops) and the marque continued with a handful of the previous team to keep things going.

But sadly the true heart of the company had gone and the new heart did not beat for long. A company such as County is more than just a product. It needs people, and it's people that make it what it is. County Commercial Cars certainly had the magic ingredient and I feel privileged to have been part of that.

Today it is very heartening to see so many highly enthusiastic people - that word again – who are so passionate about County. Since the County company departed in its various forms County products have held their heads up high. I recall going to the National Forest Machinery demo some years ago and one would have thought that the County company was still fully up and running! There were so many Countys there, many looking 'as new' all working away.

Now, some years on, there are very many Countys still hard at work but as they get older they are now becoming 'collectable'. I guess a dilemma will face their many owners as to whether to work them or keep them for posterity! A hard one.

But once again it is back to the people. This time not those that work for the company, although a few of those are still about and maintain a close interest, but all those owners and users who remain passionate about the County products. Clearly the County will be around for a long time to come. ■

Opposite page top: Tim Kirkland and a group from Ford South Africa in front of County's tour demo truck, an Oshkosh, driven by 'Joe'.

Opposite page bottom: John Hull with the restored Jubilee 1174 at the 2005 County Day in Devon.

Below: A Cameco 405 on the Hippo Valley sugar estate in southern Zimbabwe. This was replaced by 1454s.

The history of County goes back into the 1920s and is one of innovation, way ahead of its time. There were some very inventive,

County action 2003

The second County tractors day, on 13 September 2003, was organised by various local County owners in the small Devon village of Tedburn St. Mary. Howard Sherren looks at some of the models that stood out from the crowd.

It was estimated that over 100 tractors turned up to the event, well over the expected value. Nearly every shape and model of County tractor was on show, accompanied by other various unusual Ford conversions. Primarily organised by Roger Cann, Nick Martin and Robert Beer, the events success confirms it's highly likely for more future events.

Starting with the biggest, it was the first time that a large group of 1474 and 1884 tractors had been gathered together. The five, very impressive 188hp 1884 models were owned kindly shown by Roger Cann, Byron Dowd, Chris Tolley/Bill Mitchell, Andy Taylor and Nigel Anstee.

Alongside these monsters were five 1474 tractors, three of which were the older,

compact 'short-nose' versions based on the Ford 9700 and TW-20. The two 'long-nose' 1474 tractors were brought down by Russell Soper and Byron Dowd, who also displayed a 'short-nose' version. Chris Tolley and Bill Mitchell won best original tractor with one of his two 'short-nose' 1474s.

Other tractors to impress were 1184 models from Mr T Flay and Andy Cox. Mr Flay's older 'V' registered 1184 gave a good show, demonstrating its capabilities on a wide chisel plough and a power harrow. The newer 1989 registered 1184 belonging to Andy Cox had just been completely restored after spending most of it's life in a forest.

Bought in 1995 with 2,400 hours on the clock from Chatsworth Park, the tractor was fitted with a roof mounted crane for forestry use. Worked up till 2 years ago, the tractor was replaced with a new Valmet and therefore retired at 6000 hours. After 12

months of hard work, Andy and friend Jon Ball fully restored the tractor to its former glory.

At the other end of the range, co-organisers of the event Robert Beer and Nick Martin displayed an excellent 1970 1124, a 7700 Four and Ford 5000. These tractors were restored to an extremely high standard and made an excellent display working together.

Machines from other manufacturers included models from Muir-Hill, Doe and Roadless. Jon Ball displayed his very impressive Muir-Hill 171 on a 7-furrow reversible plough which completed a lot of acres in very little time.

Two Doe Triple-Ds impressed the crowds with some steady ploughing of several fields. For all those who didn't turn up, the next event was held 2 years later and was even bigger.

Nick Martin aboard a 1970 1124 putting it through its paces on a 5-furrow plough. Co-owned by Nick, and Robert Beer, the restoration was to a very high standard and was finished just in time for the event.

At almost 900hp, this line-up of modern County tractors made a very impressive sight. The stars of the show, the 1474 'long-nose' and 1884 models which are most sought after and achieve excellent resale prices. From left to right, Byron Dowd's 1474, Russell Soper's 1474, Byron Dowd's 1884, Chris Tolley's 1884 and Roger Cann's 1884. Two other 1884s made an appearance which weren't shown in the photo.

Rescued from forestry duties, this late 1989 'G' registered model was owned and restored by Andy Cox with help from Jon Ball. Believed to be one of the last tractors to be produced by County Tractors, the tractor's serial number is 5082.

In an excellent condition was this 1184 owned by Mr T Flay, who tackled some power harrowing towards the end of the event. The 1184 used the TW10 engine which was rated at 120hp.

Winning the best original tractor in a restored or unrestored condition was Bill Mitchell and Chris Tolley (middle and right). Pictured here in front of their two 1474 and 1884 models. Handing over a prize of 754 model was the builder of these specialist models Harold Powlton, who travelled all the way from Kendal.

1972 saw the launch of the 145hp 1454, based on a six cylinder, turbocharged Ford 9000 tractor. Several 1454s made an appearance, with this tractor being the only one to tackle some ploughing owned by Roger Cann.

Travelling all the way from Powys in Wales, Martyn Nicholls brought his late 974 down to join in the ploughing. ■

County action 2005

It was two years since the first major Devon County Day which impressed everyone by its popularity and excellent turn out, so the second official event had a lot to live up to. Howard Sherren was there to take it all in.

The weekend of 10-11 September 2005 saw even more Ford conversions flock to the small village of Crockenhall, located a few minutes from Tedburn St. Mary where the last event was held.

The Saturday saw around a hundred tractors arrive to a very damp site where just getting onto the field was a challenge for many of the hauliers. The weather continued to worsen and ground conditions slowly deteriorated. Though by 2pm the rain had ceased and the fields soon partially drained ready for ploughing. But the wet conditions also made more work for the event organisers, who did an excellent over the weekend directing traffic and keeping the road clear of mud and debris.

The year's event saw a wider variety of Ford based machines on show, with many more exhibitors travelling from all corners of the United Kingdom. The furthest exhibitor could have been Andrew Anderson who travelled down from North of Carlisle in Scotland to exhibit his County models and promote the Scottish County Club.

Of the hundred or so tractors which turned up, four were Doe Triple-Ds. Three were based on the Fordson Major while the other was a 130 model based on the 5000. Many were impressed by the 130, which was owned by Paul Cornwall from Lancashire, who borrowed a plough for the event and gave ploughing a go for the first time.

Other impressive machines included a County 1174 and 1184, each with a push-pull plough combination. Both were owned by Phil Smith who came down all the way from Yorkshire. The tractors proved very expensive to transport to the event, but it shows the commitment by some enthusiasts to support the event. The tractors handled seven furrows surprisingly with ease up the steep banks and the pair made a unique site while working in tandem.

Rob Morgan travelled down from Craven Arms, Shropshire with his County Super 4 and put it hard to work with three furrows. Other tractors which stood out from the rest were a cabless County 1454 and Ford 8600 4WD owned by Luke Furse from North Devon. The pair was restored to near concours condition and looked as new.

Jon Ball and Andy Cox from Cornwall showed off their County 1884, which had just been finished being built. The tractor impressed the crowds as it handled a seven-furrow reversible without a struggle on some of the steepest inclines. Although it was not original, the tractor looked and worked as good as the real thing. Andy also put his 1989 1184 to work with a very cheap Dowdeswell four-furrow reversible and produced a good result.

Mark Soper had a play on his 1454 and Kverneland conventional plough, which were perfectly matched in this terrain. A very untidy, original looking 1004, with a rough-sounding engine still managed to pull a conventional four-furrow without too much difficulty. Belonging to Adrian Ford from Crediton, this machine was one of the most orginal, 'working' clothed machines on display.

Terry Bowden and John Dennis from Tedburn brought along a 1184 and 1174 respectively. Both had owned their tractors for two years and each machine was in superb condition. Using Dowdeswell DP8 four-furrow ploughs, the pair produced some excellent ploughing on some of the steepest banks.

Some tractors were just basic Ford models and not conversions, though many were eye catchers.

A 1986 Ford TW-35 Force 2 used by Adrian Caunter on a Rabe four-furrow was in an excellent original order after covering around 6,000 hours. Russell Soper's 1993 Ford 8830 pulled the biggest plough, a eight-furrow reversible which became a challenge to use in some of the smaller fields.

David Cook from Epping, Essex gave his mint condition 7000 some stick with three furrows behind it. Although two-wheel drive, the tractor still pulled remarkably well and went everywhere that the four-wheel drives did.

Special thanks went to Mr and Mrs J Strong & Sons who hosted the event on their farm in Crockenhall. Members of the County and Ford Conversion Club should also be praised for their hard work in organising the event and keeping it running it in such difficult weather conditions.

With clouds looming, the weather was pretty horrendous but there was still a good turn out.

Rob Morgan travelled from Shropshire to take part in the event with his trusty Super-4.

Push-pull ploughs made an appearance on both 1174 and 1184 models.

Byron Dowd covered some ground in his impressive and original 1884.

Jon Ball built this particular 1884 from scratch using a Ford TW-35 and 1454 parts.

This gold 1174 is owned by A.T. Osborne and was originally used by County for the fiftieth anniversary promotional work.

Terry Bowden's 1184 is in extremely good condition and totally original. ■

A notable collection

Paul Jackson talks to Peter D Simpson about his fine array of tractors.

Plant hire specialist Paul Jackson, who operates across Cheshire and Lancashire, has been a tractor enthusiast for more years than he would like to remember. He explained with his demanding business he uses a wide array of machines and also acquires many unusual and interesting examples, especially on the draining and ditching side of the operation.

On a list of such machinery, County tractors are extremely prominent. Not wanting to dispose of, or even having to scrap, any of these classic and sometimes unusual machines Paul has built up an impressive number of both wheeled and tracked tractors in more than ten years of acquisition.

As noted, the main theme of the collection is County tractors. Many of the examples

in the collection have also been used by Paul in his business, while others have been purchased along the way. Paul says each tractor has its own story, such as the role it may have played in a particular operation. Some of the tractors are still regularly worked.

Paul's favourite is a 1972 County 1454 with Hara cab. "'This 145hp tractor is the most powerful and the most genuine of all my collection. Powered by a turbocharged Ford 9000 engine with a 9000 transmission the tractor has not been tampered with and has only 2,255 hours on the clock. For most of its life it was working on golf courses moving irrigation pipes and pulling a mole plough. It is a great tractor that has never been used to its full potential. The Boughton winch on the rear is fully functional and the tractor is equipped with tyres all round that were hardly 10 per cent worn."

Another favourite with Paul is his 1978

County 1174. Paul has used this particular tractor for several years on trailer work hauling stone. The 1174 is in original condition with very few bumps or delves to the tinwork, the paintwork is very good and the tyres are probably no more than 25 per cent worn.

Two further tractors which Paul continues to work with are a 1975 Ford 7000 with sound cab, good tyres and very good tin work. This example has 4,809 hours on the clock and is a splendid farm tractor. The other, a 1968 Ford 5000 which is still in regular work, has been used in the past for fertiliser work. It has been well looked after and despite the paintwork looking slightly rough, the tin work is excellent.

Some of the more unusual tractors in the collection include an early Diesel Major with JCB loader; this machine is a genuine JCB conversion and carries the appropriate JCB serial plate.

Paul Jackson's impressive line-up of Fords and derivatives.

Right: Based on a Ford 6600, the 1979 County 762H has a genuine 493 hours on the clock.

A very rare yellow industrial County 854T from around 1967/68 is a non-runner. It was Paul's intention to fully restore this particular machine but, sadly, time has not allowed. The tractor is complete, although the turbocharger has been removed. The 854T evolved from the 654. It was fitted with a CAV turbocharger to boost the power to 85hp but the model was only produced for one year.

A fine specimen which is complete and in working order is a yellow Howard Trench Digger on Rotopeds. This machine is based on a 1967 pre-Force Ford 5000. Paul found this particular example on a small farm in Wales when he went to do some contract work.

The farmer had originally used it for drainage work; however it had been little used and was then parked up. The machine is in very good condition, the Rotoped tracks are complete with very little wear, nothing a drop of diesel and some oil wouldn't cure.

A 1979 County Hi-Drive 762H 2WD is based on a Ford 6600 tractor. This particular model is an unusual find in Cheshire as the design is far more suited to the flat fields of Lincolnshire or the southwest. This example is as supplied by County and not a later conversion. It has only done 493 hours and spent all its working life on one farm with crop spraying as its sole job. This particular tractor would be a great asset to any County collection. Be warned – it is not a tractor to be driven and steered on hilly fields! ➡

Text: Photo: Name Surname

Below: The 1972/73 County 1454 has a genuine 2,255 hours on the clock and all four tyre are virtually unused.

The star of the collection must be the all-original 1958 Doe Power Major better known as a Doe Dual Power. It is one of only three Does built in 1958. The gears have to be selected manually on the front unit and the high-low gear lever can be selected via a system of link rods from the operator's seat, rather than the system used on later models with the front gear change through a system of master and slave cylinders. The steering is original but still gives a good response.

Paul says: "I came across this tractor by accident, I went to see a County Skid Steer and while talking to the owner he told me he had a Doe and asked if I would be interested in buying it. And, as they say, the rest is history. The Doe came back to Macclesfield and apart from keeping it running I have done very little to it. It is as original as you can get." ■

The County set

Mike Gormley went to the County factory on a school visit and was hooked. He joined the company and tells us what it was like to work for the of the country's most innovative firms.

I was extremely lucky. I joined County (County Commercial Cars Ltd) as a salesman more or less direct from college. My first encounter with the firm was while at school in Hampshire when our school's Young Farmers Club went for a factory visit, which left a lasting impression. I still have a photo I took of a County Crawler outside the Albert Street factory. Little did I realise that this was to become the hub of my life in a few years time.

I tried to pursue an agricultural career and, following two years of farm work and association with a pair of Roadless 95s' I went to the Royal Agricultural College at Cirencester. It was here, as secretary of the Machinery Club, that I fixed up a lecture on County Tractors.

Peter Jaggard (sales manager and Don Mole (field operations manager gave the talk and, as you do at that time of life, I suggested that they might like to employ me after college. The result, to my surprise, was a preliminary interview.

There was a job coming up, but before my time at college was due to end, so I had to be patient. There was to be another opportunity in a year or so. I rather liked the idea of working for County so I went off to gain more practical experience on farms to absorb that year. During my time at college I worked for Alvan Blanch (Corn Dryers) near Cirencester who ran a number of Countys on their associated farms. Proudly I had 'my' Super-4 for some of this time. There were two 1124s and a 1004 as well. The farm had a lot of poor wet land and we often worked as a team with the Countys to do the best we could to cultivate the difficult areas.

I got all the really bad bits as the Super-4 was lighter and smaller and I did not care if I got stuck – which I remember I did fairly often when trying to get through near-bogs to try to cultivate them dry. Those days were a challenge but I was being paid to enjoy myself. I was also learning a lot and have continued to operate vehicles in difficult conditions ever since.

The time came for another interview, this time with the 'big boss', Brian Taylor, the sales director. I remember the day quite well. My car broke down in the car park and Brian not only paid for my petrol to get to the interview but also offered to get me home if my car did not work. I could not believe what I was hearing: these seemed to be good people. I was right.

On September 1, 1970 I joined the company, the same day as the safety cab became a legal requirement in the UK. ➡

Tim Kirkland in a familiar work pose – on a steep slope on a 754, cultivating a cane field in Zululand Natal.

Mike Gormley (driving) with Aubrey Gouws (sales manager Ford South Africa) and Keith Berning (director of tractor operations South Africa) in 1980.

My patience had been rewarded and I discovered that I had 'fast tracked' into this type of job. All other 'field people' had come via dealers or Ford. I was very green.

I was soon involved in a training programme. This took me into the factory on the assembly line, the development shop and driving endlessly around the MIRA high speed circuit at all of three miles an hour, testing a newly developed second gear. This was much more interesting than it sounds!

I was soon off around the country and into a world of extensive travel and living in

hotels with most of the salesmen and service engineers. I spent time with Tim Kirkland in the west and Bruce Keech in the east. I was a bit disappointed not to go up with Jock Hairs in Scotland but I did spend some time with Ken Ree and Johnny Heathers for an insight into the service side.

Very early on I recall being involved in a ploughing marathon where we ploughed with a 4000/4 for 24 hours, fuelling and driver changing on the move (would not be allowed now) and only stopping twice to re point the plough. The record was broken.

Life became more serious when I began to concentrate on what was to be my area, the whole of southern England. Vernon Ponting was soon to retire and then it would be my responsibility. Vernon took me under his wing for a few weeks and then headed off into the sunset in Cornwall to enjoy his cliff top retirement.

As the southern area was also the one in which Fleet was situated I had a lot of contact with base and so tended to become involved with some of the other activities such as demo tours and major shows, promotional activities, such as photo shoots and film making. 'This meant I got to work with 'Huller', John Hull the company demonstrator.

It very soon became apparent that 'County People' were held in high regard. Walk into most dealers or visit a customer and say you were from County - and that was it, you were 'someone'. It was very good and, for a rocky rep, something of a relief. This attitude, I was to find out in time, was more or less worldwide.

In-house, County was perhaps a little old fashioned. Whenever a director entered a room people stood up. In general they were addressed as 'sir'. However right throughout the company there was a definite team sprit. Most people got on and worked well together. The people on the assembly line, in the stores, in the drawing office, in the development shop were always interested in what was going on in the outside world. They were pleased to help if you had a problem or needed something.

John Hull undertaking the first trial of the 754 Fintrack in Fleet Pond.

Mike after a dusty demonstration in New Zealand.

Mike operating an 1174 on dual wheels on a steep slope in New Zealand. Ford's Alan Lash looks on.

The others and I often brought potential customers and dealers to Fleet for factory visit and visitors frequently commented on the atmosphere there. During the tour they were often drawn into conversations with the people on the assembly line that were genuinely interested in what 'their' tractors were to be used for and where they were going. With an export market of some 75 per cent the build cards were mostly for overseas destinations and were quite often for some strange build.

County thrived on the unusual and the innovative. Agriculture was of course a major market but Countys went off to work in more applications and countries than you could imagine. I seem to recall that some 120 countries were 'on the books'. Knowledge of geography was a must.

Generally the outside team and the associated office-based sales and service people only came together for the occasional meetings and the Royal and Smithfield Shows. These were the principal events for the company. The evenings were somewhat social and usually very humorous and the days mostly long and busy. These times were something of a challenge to constitution and endurance but there was a great atmosphere within the team. Once you were a County man, few ever considered moving on. ∎

Going across the slope operating a Howard 120" rotavator.

Coastal Countys

Roger Hamlin finds tractors that help bring a delicacy to your table.

Castlepoint is a small beachside town on New Zealand's North Island. It is home to Castle Rock, a lighthouse, an annual horserace meeting - and a fleet of County tractors.

It is reached from a road that winds past large farms and plantations of pine trees until it ends in sand dunes. As I walked across these I saw the biggest boat trailers I have ever seen, all but two of them loaded with boats, which were about 50 feet long and driven by Hamilton jet engines.

The trailers were about 15 feet longer than the boats and coupled to County tractors, which pushed the trailers into the shallow water until the boats floated off.

The boats are used in the crayfish industry and each holds a valuable quota as the crustaceans are sought-after all over the world, which explains why so much equipment is employed on work which may only last two months a year if the crayfish are running well.

The Countys' life in this environment is between 10 and 12 years.

Looking towards the bay the boats go into before powering out to sea just in front of the big rock. This entrance is called the Gap. What a line-up of County tractors .

Right: With Countys becoming harder to find, is this the future?

Dean Hatchard and his family have been fishing here many years and he now looks after this side of the operation.

He said the main reason why most of these dual-wheeled County tractors were used was because the gearboxes were fully sealed and so protected against penetration by sea water.

Nevertheless, they require quite a lot of maintenance; the biggest problem being starter motors and alternators.

The tyres are filled with water to provide extra traction on the sandy beach. Crawlers are not used because they would carve up the sand to a higher degree. ■